THE FLOWERS
OF
CRETE

TEXT BY
MARINA CLAUSER

PHOTOS BY
ANDREA INNOCENTI

BONECHI

Contents

Publication created and designed by Casa Editrice Bonechi
Project manager Monica Bonechi
Photographic research by Alberto Andreini
Graphics and layout by Maria Rosanna Malagrinò
Editing by Patrizia Fabbri and Giorgio Montinari

Text by Marina Clauser
Translation by Paula Boomsliter

© Copyright by Casa Editrice Bonechi, via Cairoli 18/b Firenze - Italia
Tel +39 055576841 - Fax +39 0555000766
E-mail:bonechi@bonechi.it - Internet:www.bonechi.it
Printed in Italy by Centro Stampa Editoriale Bonechi.

ISBN 88-8029-970-0

* * *

INTRODUCTION

Crete, the fifth largest island in the Mediterranean, is located equidistant from Europe, Asia and Africa. Its most outstanding features are its lengthy coastline, high mountains, fertile plains, extensive hilly areas, and stupendous gorges.

The about 1000 km of coastline include both sandy beaches and high cliffs, with more and less pronounced peninsulas on the northern shore and many small islands; the northern coastlines are generally more accessible, while those to the south are often characterized by steep cliffs.

The most important mountains are Mount Ida, Crete's highest, which rises in the center of the island with its peak, Psiloritis, at 2456 meters; Lefká Óri (White Mountains), rising to 2452 meters in the western portion of the island; and Mount Díkti, 2148 meters high and located to the east. In the easternmost part of the island is the Sitía range, which rises to 1476 meters. Other highlands, although not as prominent, cover a large portion of the territory of Crete and within them are found broad highland and fertile plains areas like Omalós, Messará, Nida and Lassíthi. The substrate of the island is 85% calcareous rock, and due to the frequency of karst phenomena there are many grottoes and gorges.

The gorges are one of the most spectacular natural features of Crete: they are generally north-south rifts in the mountains that cross most of the island's width, with tall, steep, almost parallel walls at the base of which run watercourses that generally dry up in the summer. It is in the gorges and the highest areas of the mountainous areas that we find the majority of the plants endemic to Crete.

The watercourses are few, and those few there are are often dry from early summer onward. The wet areas include the Lake of Kournas, near Georgioupoli, and the man-made reservoir of Agía near Haniá. Despite their quite limited extension, these environments are of great importance in that they provide a stopping-place between Africa and Europe for migrating birds.

The climate is typically Mediterranean, with hot summers with only rare episodes of precipitation from May to October, and mild winters with greatest rainfall in December and January. Average annual rainfall on the northern coast is 700 mm, while on the much more arid southern coast it averages only 200-300 mm.

Local climatic conditions are strongly influenced by the nearness of the high mountains to the coast; in summer, haze may form on the north-facing slopes, which are damper than the areas with southern exposure.

Snow persists on the highest peaks until summer; the spectacle offered by typically Mediterranean flowers blooming in the summer against snow-capped pinnacles is particularly evocative.

The prevailing winds are the west wind from the Atlantic, the hot, dry Saharan sirocco, and the meltémi, winds from central Asia that blow at sometimes annoying strength on the northern coast to mitigate temperatures that would otherwise be extreme.

During the Miocene era (26-25 million years ago), when

Beaches, mountains, and gorges are the most significant elements of the landscape of Crete.

Beaches, mountains, and gorges are the most significant elements of the landscape of Crete. Ferula communis in flower against the backdrop of the snow-capped mountains of Crete (right); intensive cultivation (right, below).

the climate was warmer than it is today, there emerged in the area now occupied by the Aegean Sea a vast territory of which today's Crete is but a fragment. In the mid Miocene (18 million years ago), Crete was part of an unbroken strip of land linking continental Greece, the Aegean islands, and Turkey.

During the late Miocene, the Mediterranean Sea dried up a number of times. Toward the end of the Tertiary period (10 million years ago), the dry land underwent a number of changes due to sudden lowering or more prolonged geological phenomena: the sea invaded the land and the landmass broke up. Thus, for example, eight million years ago what is now Crete was instead a group of several islands: today's highest mountain peaks.

In the Pliocene era (3 million years ago), the landmass alternately lifted and sank, causing tectonic fractures; Crete was still a group of islands during this period. Finally, during the Pleistocene (about 1 million years ago), the island took on its present form.

Geological events have played a fundamental role in the evolution of the flora and fauna of the island: since the Mediterranean Sea has dried up repeatedly over the course of geological history, Crete has more than once been in communication with southern Greece, southwestern Turkey, and with such islands as Kythera, Antikythera, Rhodes, and the Cyclades, and this fact favored the migration of the plants from one part to another of whatever was the dry landmass at any given time.

The repeated glaciations that alternated with interglacial periods through the Pleistocene were also very important in determining plant distribution: the formation of ice, with the consequent lowering of the level of the sea (it has been calculated that during the first glacial periods - Gunz, Mindel, and Riss - the level of the sea was lower than it is today by hundreds of meters), created bridges linking widely-scattered territories and so facilitated the migration of plants and animals.

There were also periods in geological history, other than our own, during which Crete was completely isolated and many existing species differentiated to produce new subspecies or even new species.

That these geomorphological processes actually took place is confirmed by the presence, on Crete, of many elements native to the Balkan region and to Asia, as for example Ebenus cretica *and* Ricotia cretica, *endemic species belonging*

to genera the distribution center of which is in Asia.

Most of the endemics are ancient species that were once widely distributed over the island and which, isolated by the various inundations of the Mediterranean, succeeded in surviving while their congeners disappeared: emblematic in this sense is the case of Petromarula pinnata, *a monospecific genus endemic to Crete. It has been calculated that the isolation of the island lasted about five and one-half million years: despite the length of this geological period, only a few species evolved* in loco, *probably due both to a shortage of new habitats that the new species could colonize and to strong competition among the existing species. Only when the ice withdrew did vast territories open to conquest by the plains species most ready to invade them.*

THE FLORA

The natural beauties of Crete, the "fair wooded island" as it was called by Homer in the Odyssey, Crete the "windy" isle, have been sung since antiquity. Herodotus speaks of an island covered with shade trees; it is no coincidence that the name of the central mountains of Crete, Ida, derives from the Doric idha = forest. The forests in fact covered almost the entire territory of the island and supplied precious material as early as the Minoan period for construction of palaces, and under Venetian rule, for ships and fortifications. Forest fires, grazing, and indiscriminate use of the land by man have nevertheless greatly reduced the forested acreage over the centuries.

Today, the territory of Crete is in the main exploited for agriculture and grazing: in the highlands, in the fertile plains, and in the areas in which the lay of the land and climatic conditions permit, intensive cultivation produces citrus fruits, bananas, vegetables, grapes, almonds, figs, and other products destined for the foreign as well as the domestic markets. In order to achieve greater competitiveness on the market, plastic-covered greenhouses are often used; by now, these constructions have become normal, albeit not aesthetically pleasing, elements of the landscape. Abandoned terracing and windmills in working order and in disuse remind the visitor of the great importance that has been vested by agriculture since the most remote times.

Agriculture is flanked in importance by herding: goats and sheep are to be found literally everywhere on Crete, where almost 50% of the territory is given over to pastures.

Unfortunately, however, the sheep and above all the goats destroy many of the plants, so that in the end the typical vegetation of the island is represented mainly by garrigue and phrygana formations characterized by spiny, highly aromatic graze-resistant plants.

The other element that has modified the natural landscape is the extensive urbanization that has taken place on the island mainly in response to the tourist demand: kilometer after kilometer of the territory, especially along the northern coast, is by now entirely occupied by buildings and tourist complexes - and the building continues.

Of the ancient and famous forests sung by the poets there remain only limited extensions of Pinus brutia, Italian Cypress, and the spiny Kermes Oak. Nevertheless, Crete still possesses an unquestionable charm, not only thanks to its architectural treasures, the authentic hospitality of its people, and the renowned vacation spots, but also to its natural beauty.

The tourist whose curiosity is aroused by the rich plant life of the island is never disappointed. Above all in the spring the visitor to Crete can admire many different and some very particular plants in full bloom as he travels to beaches, gorges, mountains, and the archaeological sites and castle ruins.

The vastly assorted flora of Crete counts more than 1700 species with distributions from the beaches to the highest mountains; to these we must add the about 70 plants introduced in various periods of history from other countries; many of these have become naturalized. There are numerous endemics (about 10% of the total), the majority of which are found in the gorges and in the high mountains; that is, in the most inaccessible environments and therefore those richest in 'natural' vegetation.

The climate of the island is marked by its scarce rainfall, high summer temperatures, and strong winds; moreover, the soil is incapable of holding the moisture provided by precipitation. There thus are created arid conditions that the perennial plants are able to withstand only thanks to specific adaptations that limit the transpiration of water, like hairiness and leaves that are small and leathery or caducous during the dry season. Other adaptations, like the development of thorns and production of highly aromatic substances, discourage the grazing animals. Many plants flower in the spring, when climatic conditions are most favorable, and live through the driest season in the form of underground organs such as bulbs, tubers, or rhizomes (geophytes), or as seeds. The arboreal species on Crete are relatively few, only about a dozen, while the prevailing plant type is the xerophytic shrub with its special adaptations for withstanding the aridity of the climate and the grazing animals; the geophytes are also many in number. Today's vegetation and flora therefore represent the result of geological events, climatic influences, and the prolonged and complex action exerted by man on his environment.

This guide examines the flowers botany enthusiasts will be most likely to see during their stay as visitors to Crete. In order to aid species recognition, the plants have been grouped by environments: coastal communities (sandy and rocky coasts), woodlands, maquis, garrigues and phrygana, rupestrian habitats, gorges, wet areas, and lands that have felt the effects of anthropization (roadsides, old walls, cultivated and abandoned farmland).

Only naturally, many plants are common to more than one environment. This is true above all for the phrygana, where we will find many of the plants listed as living in the garrigues, and for the gorges, composite environments that host the plants that typically live on cliffs and along watercourses.

Certain of the plants listed are rare or endangered, or thrive in habitats worthy of conservation. For this reason we have included the relative European Community environmental protection provisions as set forth in the EUROPEAN COUNCIL DIRECTIVE 92/43/EEC of 21 May 1992 'on the conservation of natural habitats and of wild fauna and flora' of naturalistic interest at the Community level (Natural Habitats Directive).

Below, windmills in the Lassíthi highland area.

5

COASTAL COMMUNITIES

Some of the most important attractions of Crete are the island's seaside localities: beautiful beaches, deeply-cut bays and inlets, high cliffs rising over the sea, and clean waters in which one can swim for much of the year. Unfortunately, however, tourism has exercised strong pressure on the environment; the consequence has been extensive, uncontrolled urbanization of the coasts. This development has caused a considerable decrease in the natural environments, to the detriment, above all, of the low-lying sandy beach habitats, but in some areas it is still possible to single out areas of great naturalistic interest with characteristic flora that is highly varied and with long flowering periods on the sandy beaches and more uniform, but no less interesting, on the coastal cliffs. The plants of the coastlines of Crete are commonly found throughout the rest of the Mediterranean as well.

SANDY COASTS

The instability of the sandy substrate and the excessive drainage on the strip of land closest to the sea make life particularly difficult for plants: only a few have proven capable of supporting the salinity and colonizing these areas just above the high tide line. These tenacious species are generally annuals, like, for example, *Cakile maritima*, a small crucifer with violet flowers.

Further inland, the substrate is only partially mobile; this fact facilitates colonization by a grass, *Ammophila arenaria*, with a well-developed root system capable of spreading for a number of meters both vertically and horizontally below the surface of the sand: the plant thus stabilizes the sand and encourages the formation of the dunes by creating conditions favorable to colonization by other plants. Further contributing to stabilizing the sandy substrate are plants that settle in the spaces left free by the gramineous species: *Otanthus maritimus*, easily recognizable thanks to its small yellow flowers but above all to the dense hairs with which it is covered; *Medicago marina*, with its numerous creeping stems and like the first-mentioned species hairy, to reduce

Above, Silene colorata *and* Rumex bucephalophorus *in flower along the seashore. Below, bushy patches of* Ammophila arenaria.

transpiration; *Eryngium maritimum*, a beautiful but especially insidious plant with large spines; *Pancratium maritimum*, which in late summer is covered with large white flowers; *Euphorbia paralias*, a small plant with erect stems; and *Cyperus capitatus*, typified by the long, rigid bracts that subtend the inflorescence. Further inland yet, where the substrate is more stable and the action of the sea is less intense, we find two plants that form extensive, densely-populated colonies and that stand out for their bright colors: *Silene colorata*, with its flowers of a beautiful intense pink, and *Rumex bucephalophorus*, with its red-and-green stems and leaves. Other plants typical of this habitat are *Anthemis rigida* subsp. *rigida*, a yellow-blossomed member of the family Compositae; two small plantains with peculiar, tiny flowers (*Plantago weldenii* and *P. bellardii*); *Matthiola tricuspidata*, a small crucifer with violet flowers; and *Ononis natrix*, a member of the Pea family (Leguminosae) that forms much-branched hemispherical bushes. The dune environments are thus revealed as areas of utmost naturalistic interest. But they also strongly threatened by anthropic pressure, and EEC Directive No. 92/43 includes them among the 'natural habitat types of Community interest'. Not far from the sea grow shrubby plants that at times form dense, almost impenetrable thickets. One typical representative of these plants is the Prickly Juniper (*Juniperus oxycedrus* subsp. *macrocarpa*).

The showiest of the beach-dwellers is doubtless the Cretan Palm (*Phoenix theophrasti*). This beautiful plant, endemic to Crete, thrives on sandy substrates in the small, humid valleys near the sea; at Väï, on the eastern tip of the island, it forms splendid stands with oleander undergrowth. Other smaller but equally decorative palm growths have been reported on the southern coast of the Rethymnon Prefecture. The palm is endangered, and is currently protected by EEC Directive 92/43 (see Enclosure); the Cretan Palm woods are considered habitats of Community interest.

Above, Cretan Palms; bottom, a brightly-colored patch of Ononis natrix.

CAKILE MARITIMA SCOP. [1]
(Cruciferae)

An annual herb with branched and prostrate or somewhat ascending stems and with fleshy, deeply-divided leaves that are sessile higher on the stem. The inflorescence is composed of elongated congested racemes of aromatic pink-violet flowers that bloom from March through June and in September-October. The fruit is a two-part siliqua long about 2 cm. This is a nitrophilous psammophile found on the sandy coasts throughout the Mediterranean basin. It possesses diuretic properties and is used in folk medicine as a cure for renal calculosis; the spicy-tasting leaves are often used as a garnish for mixed salads.

OTANTHUS MARITIMUS (L.) HOFFMANNS. & LINK [2]
(Compositae)

A small pioneering perennial that grows in the dune areas throughout the Mediterranean and exerts a stabilizing action on the sandy soils. The gender name derives from the Greek *otos* (ear) and *anthos* (flower), from the form of the corolla, which is composed of three membranous bracts that create a peculiar profile. A thick white down covers both the stems and the small oval, slightly saw-toothed alternate leaves. The globose flowerheads, with their short peduncles, are composed of an envelope of white-wooly scales around tubular yellow flowers that are visible from June through September. On Crete, the plant is found mainly on the northern coasts.

AMMOPHILA ARENARIA (L.) LINK SUBSP. *ARUNDINACEA* H. LINDB. [3]
(Graminaceae)

This graminaceous plant owes its gender name to the Greek terms *ammos* (sand) and *philos* (lover); that is, a 'sand-loving' plant; the species epithet is a Latin intensive meaning 'arenaceous' or 'sandy'. It is a herbaceous perennial that forms dense, bushy patches, often more than one meter in height, anchored to the sandy dunes by the compact, rhizomatous, creeping roots. The

1

2

narrow and somewhat inrolled culms are stout and rough with long, glaucous-green hairy leaves that are grooved on the inner and smooth and shiny on the outer surface. The flowers appear between April and June in yellowish, tapering spikes. Various subspecies of *Ammophila arenaria* are found on the dunes and the beaches of many Mediterranean and Atlantic coastlines.

MEDICAGO MARINA L. [4]
(Leguminosae)

A herbaceous perennial that is commonly found on the sandy beaches and the shoreline dunes, where it covers the soil with its intertwining prostrate stems. Dense hair lends the leaves and the

legumes a silvery-grey color. The legumes, with small spines, are spiraling pods that generally form 2 to 3 turns. The yellow flowers appear from March through May in rounded, compact inflorescences.

3

ERYNGIUM MARITIMUM L. ⑤
(Umbelliferae)

Although not overly frequent,
the Sea Holly, with its large blue-
green leaves with undulate spiny
margins, may be seen on the dunes
and on the sandy beaches.
The blue flowers appear from
March through July in dense,
globose heads surrounded
at the base by wide, spiny bracts.
The roots are edible; in ancient
times, the Greek physician
Dioscurides prescribed the roots
as a cure for flatulence.

PANCRATIUM MARITIMUM L. ⑥
(Amaryllidaceae)

Known by the common English
names of Sea Daffodil or Sea Lily,
this perennial has thick, flat,
ribbon-shaped leaves, 2 to 4 cm
wide, often showing one or more
twists in the blade. It flowers from
August through October with large,
fragrant, very showy white flowers;
their beauty inspired the ancient
wall paintings of the palaces at
Knossos on Crete and Thera on
Santorini.
This plant is distributed throughout
the Mediterranean basin, but since
it is the object of indiscriminate
picking it is becoming somewhat
rare.

EUPHORBIA PARALIAS L. ⑦
(Euphorbiaceae)

The species name of the Sea Spurge
derives from the Greek *paralios*
(near the water). It is a glabrous
perennial herb, green-grey in color.
The stiff, erect stems, which reach
50 cm height, bear numerous
pointed, linear leaves that are set

4

5

close together or partially
overlapping. The umbellate terminal
inflorescences of the members of
the Spurge family are called cyathia
and are made up of a variable
number of rays each bearing
flowers of a single sex; the male
flowers are arranged around the
females and the whole is

surrounded by an envelope
of bracts of varying form.
The spherical inflorescence,
with 3 to 6 rays, is surrounded by
concave oval bracts. The plant
flowers in April and May. Although
it is found on the dunes throughout
the Mediterranean, it is relatively
rare on Crete.

6

7

8

9

10

CYPERUS CAPITATUS VAND. [8]
(Cyperaceae)

A perennial plant typical of the interdunal depressions, with an erect, channeled stem that rises from a long, creeping rhizome. The leaves are narrow and linear; the flowers (March-April) form brownish spikelets arranged in a globose terminal inflorescence subtended by 1 to 3 rigid bracts up to 15 cm in length. *C. capitatus* is quite rare on Crete.

SILENE COLORATA POIR. SUBSP. COLORATA [9]
(Caryophyllaceae)

A variable, short-lasting annual with erect or prostrate stems. The leaves are linear to oblong. The flowers are a showy deep pink with lobed petals and a club-shaped calyx; they can be seen from March through May.
This plant often forms extensive and highly-decorative populations on the sandy or rocky coasts, but it can also be found far from the sea on sandy substrates.

RUMEX BUCEPHALOPHORUS L. [10]
(Polygonaceae)

A small, highly-variable plant, generally annual, with simple or branched wiry stems. The small leaves are lanceolate or elliptical.
The reddish to red flowers are also very small and are borne in racemes or spikes; the reddish flower stalks may be either slender and short or long and thick. *R. bucephalophorus* L. forms extensive populations on the sandy and rocky coasts, and it can also be found in other areas in moist soils and growing in the gravel of the riverbeds.

ANTHEMIS RIGIDA (SM.) BOISS. EX HELDR. SUBSP. RIGIDA [11]
(Compositae)

A small plant growing to 15 cm, with pinnate or two-pinnately-lobed oblong leaves, the segments of which are linear or lanceolate. The tubular yellow flowers form flowerheads 3 to 9 mm in diameter in April and May. This plant lives in sandy or rocky areas at altitudes of up to 2200 meters.

11 →

PLANTAGO WELDENII RHB. SUBSP. *WELDENII* 12
(Plantaginaceae)

Differently from the next-described species, this Plantain has reddish-green leaves that are divided into narrow segments, and cylindrical inflorescences, larger than the leaves, composed of small flowers that are visible between March and May. This hairy plant thrives on rocky substrates; although it generally grows near the sea, it may also be found at altitudes of up to 1000 meters.

PLANTAGO BELLARDII ALL. 13
(Plantaginaceae)

This small Plantain is easily recognizable thanks to its dark-colored, entire, linear-lanceolate leaves, up to 7 cm long, that form a basal rosette. The flowers, insignificant to the naked eye, can be observed with the aid of a magnifying glass: they appear, forming beautiful geometric designs in dense conical inflorescences, in April and May. The sepals have scarious margins; the anterior sepals are almost completely detached. All parts of the plant are hairy. It can also be found in the open spaces of the phrygana formations.

13

MATTHIOLA TRICUSPIDATA (L.) R. BR. IN W.T. AITON 14
(Cruciferae)

A greyish-downy annual with a stout base and herbaceous shoots. The four-petaled flowers (March-April) are light pink to violet in color. The fruit is a siliqua up to 10 cm long, terminating in a three-horned apex formed by the residue of the stigma; hence the species name. Besides on the sandy and rocky coasts, the plant also thrives on old walls; on Crete, it is found mainly along the northern coast.

15

ONONIS NATRIX L. [15]
(Leguminosae)

This glandular-hairy (sticky) subshrub, with a somewhat unpleasant odor, forms densely-branched hemispherical cushions. The leaves are each divided into three toothed segments. The flowers (March-July) are papilionaceous (resembling a butterfly or a bow-tie) and yellow, veined with purple on the outside; they are borne on long stalks with pointed appendices.

JUNIPERUS OXYCEDRUS L. SUBSP. MACROCARPA (SM.) BALL [16] [17]
(Cupressaceae)

A shrub with twisted branches and spine-tipped needle-like leaves up to 2.5 cm long, with two whitish bands along the upper surface. The fleshy brown cones, called galbuli, may be up to 1.5 cm in diameter (the subspecies name in fact derives from the Greek *macro* = large, and *carpos* = fruit). The leaves and the galbuli boast diuretic properties; the fragrant and durable wood has been used for inlays and objects turned on the lathe. The Prickly Juniper lives near the coasts on sandy or rocky soils, and forms beautiful, dense populations that are almost true woods both on the island of Hrissí facing Ierápetra and on

16

Elafoníssi off western Crete. These Prickly Juniper formations on the sandy coasts and maritime rocks are habitats of Community interest.

PHOENIX THEOPHRASTI GREUTER [18]
(Palmae)

This beautiful palm, named after Theophrastus, is mentioned by Homer in his description of the birth of Apollo in the shade of palm trees introduced to Delos from Crete, apparently by Theseus, the hero who defeated the Minotaur. The Cretan Palm grows as tall as 15 meters, with more or less prominently arched secondary stems that determine its distinctively elegant form. At the summit are the compound leaves, which grow to 2 meters in length. The fruits appear only on mature individuals.

17

18

MARITIME CLIFFS AND
ROCKY COASTAL AREAS

On the seaside cliffs, where the salt spray continually wets the surface of the rock, only highly specialized, salt-resistant plants capable of living in the cracks in the stone can survive. It is in similar situations that we encounter the chasmophytes, including *Crithmum maritimum L.*, an umbellifer with fleshy leaves, and various species of *Limonium* that are highly diversified from area to area.

In the rocky areas near the sea, in the crevices in the cliffs, grow minute plants capable developing roots in the rock. These so-called lithophytes include *Paronychia macrosepala*, with its silvery overtones, *Silene sedoides*, with its reddish, fleshy leaves, and the densely hairy *Anthemis ammanthus* subsp. *paleacea*. Certain plants are found on both rocky and sandy substrates: for example, *Spergularia bocconei*, *Reichardia picroides*, and some Sea Heaths. The Mediterranean rocky coast plant communities, with various species of *Limonium* and *Euphorbia* and with *Crithmum maritimum* and *Silene sedoides*, are of Community interest.

CRITHMUM MARITIMUM L. 19
(Umbelliferae)

This plant, with its fleshy leaves, is a true chasmophyte that lives on vertical cliffs, and is widely distributed throughout Crete. The flowers, with small yellow petals, appear from August through October, grouped in umbels. The inflorescences dry on the plant and persist through the winter. The leaves are edible if harvested before the flowering period, and are eaten raw in small quantities in salads or pickled: rich in vitamin C and mineral salts, they have always been valued for their tangy flavor.

19

LIMONIUM SINUATUM (L.) MILL.
SUBSP. *SINUATUM* [20]
(Plumbaginaceae)

This perennial is rough to the touch due to its stiff hairs. It may reach 40 cm in height, growing from a basal rosette of pinnately-lobed leaves, up to 10 cm in length, with sinuous margins. The stem has four membranous wings that divide into three parts in correspondence to the nodes. The flowers (April-May) have papery, violet-blue calyxes and insignificant yellowish corollas, and are grouped in dense inflorescences. All the species in the genus *Limonium* live near the sea, generally on cliffs. Certain species, like *Limonium graecum* (Poir.) Rech., recognizable thanks to its small pink flowers (July-September), are true

20

chasmophytes that live on vertical cliffs, but *Limonium sinuatum* is a lithophyte.

PARONYCHIA MACROSEPALA BOISS. [21]
(Caryophyllaceae)

A perennial herb with small, oval, grey-green opposite leaves, covered with a fine down. The small white flowers are grouped in flowerheads surrounded by silvery bracts. Grows on the dry soils of the sandy and rocky coasts.

SILENE SEDOIDES POIR. [22]
(Caryophyllaceae)

A small annual herb with stems that grow no taller than 10 cm. The densely-hairy, fleshy leaves are at most one cm long and are often flushed red. The flowers, which may be pink or whitish, appear from March through May. This plant lives near the sea, generally in the cracks between rocks; it may also be found on sandy substrates.

21

22

ANTHEMIS AMMANTHUS GREUTER SUBSP. PALEACEA GREUTER [23]
(Compositae)

This subspecies, which is endemic to Crete, is found only in the eastern portion of the island on rocky soils along the coast and on the cliffs of the small offshore islands. It is a small annual with slender stems that are whitish due to their thick hair. The minuscule leaves are fleshy; the basal leaves are stalked and the upper leaves are subsessile. The flowerheads, about 1 cm in diameter, are enclosed in sheaths formed of bracts with scarious margins and tips; the scales on the flower receptacle are hairy and pointed. The florets (April-May) are yellow and all tubular.

23

SPERGULARIA BOCCONEI (SCHEELE) GRAEBN IN ASCH. & GRAEBN [24]
(Caryophyllaceae)

An annual herb up to 25 cm in height, with slender stems bearing small leaves. The flowers (March-May) have pink petals shading to white at the base. The stem becomes hairy-glandular near the inflorescence. This plant, which is rather rare on Crete, lives on the rocky beaches, on the sandy beaches (and in this case the grains of sand attach to the stem and the leaves), and on saline soils.

24

25

REICHARDIA PICROIDES (L.) ROTH [25]
(Compositae)

A perennial that varies in height from 5 to 45 cm, with entire or pinnate basal leaves and cauline leaves that are no more than small scales. The purple-veined yellow flowers, all ligulate, appear from March through May in usually solitary flowerheads borne on stalks about 20 cm in length; each flowerhead is enveloped by a pyriform involucre formed of heart shaped bracts with membranous margins. The plant grows on the seaside cliffs and on the sandy beaches, but may also be found on old walls and in the crevices between rocks.

26

FRANKENIA PULVERULENTA L.
SUBSP. *PULVERULENTA* [26]
(Frankeniaceae)

An annual of the Sea Heath family with prostrate, occasionally ascending, finely-hairy stems. The small leaves are oval or elliptical and grooved at the center. The many tiny violet flowers appear from March through June on the lateral branches or in crowded spike inflorescences. This plant lives near the sea on both rocky and sandy substrates.

FRANKENIA HIRSUTA L. [27]
(Frankeniaceae)

This small plant is densely hairy, especially at the tops of the branches. This Sea Heath is often seen veiled in the thin layer of dust or sand that tends to deposit on the leaf blades. The white flowers appear in April in wide, dense terminal clusters.

27

MEDICAGO ARBOREA L. [28]
(Leguminosae)

This shrub, covered with a silky down, grows as tall as 4 meters. The leaves are composed of obovate segments. The flowers (February-March) are yellow, 1.2 to 1.5 cm in length, and grouped in short racemes. The fruit is a net-veined, coiled legume. *M. arborea* is native to the islands of Kárpathos and Kássos in the Dodecanese; on Crete, it is cultivated as a garden plant and is used to line roadsides; it is by now largely naturalized.

28→

29

30

MALCOLMIA FLEXUOSA (SM.) SM. 30
(Cruciferae)

A small annual with oblong, toothed leaves and purple-pink flowers tending to lighten somewhat in color toward the center, and with notched petals. The plant blooms between March and May. The long, narrow siliqua is only slightly wider than its stalk. *M. flexuosa* lives near the sea, on calcareous detritus, in cracks in rocks, and even on sandy substrates; it may also be found on old walls.

*

31

Although due to the inclemency of the environmental factors trees cannot survive on the cliffs overlooking the sea, we do find shrubs like *Juniperus phoenicea* and *Thymelaea hirsuta* that represent the first step toward the formation of the phrygana.

JUNIPERUS PHOENICEA L. 29
(Cupressaceae)

The Phoenician Juniper is a tall shrub with small cylindrical branches covered with blunt, scalelike leaves. The crown is generally pyramidal in shape, but the habit changes from erect in the more sheltered areas to prostrate in the windy, open areas. The spherical cones (galbuli) are green when young, becoming red at maturity. The Phoenician Juniper, which may be found in phrygana formations, in any case grows only near the sea.

THYMELAEA HIRSUTA (L.) ENDL. 31
(Thymelaeaceae)

A small evergreen shrub that appears greyish due to its dense hair.

The leaves are scalelike and closely imbricate; they are white-downy on the upper surface and glabrous on the lower. The flowers, with a yellow perianth, appear from October through March. This plant lives on sandy coasts or in low-altitude rocky areas; on Crete it is found prevalently in the western and central areas.

CUPRESSUS SEMPERVIRENS L. F. *HORIZONTALIS* (MILL.) VOSS 32
(Cupressaceae)

The Italian Cypress is a tree is distinguished by its densely imbricated scalelike leaves and its roundish cones or strobili, formed of 8 to 14 woody scales. It enjoys wide diffusion in the entire Mediterranean basin, but in Europe is spontaneous only on Crete in its *horizontalis* form, easily distinguishable due to its open, prostrate habit; it may form small woods, either alone or in association with other trees. The *sempervirens* form, with its branches pressed close to the trunk, is often planted in rows along roads and near cemeteries. Although usually considered primarily an ornamental plant, since ancient times the cypress has been attributed religious significance. For instance, its name drives from Kyparissos, one of the boys beloved of Apollo, who in the throes of excruciating remorse over having accidentally slain a sacred deer was transformed into a cypress tree. Moreover, since time immemorial the cypress has been prized for its precious hard wood, and its use in building has determined a considerable diminution in the natural populations; it is nevertheless still possible to see some limited-scale virgin cypress forests, mainly in the western part of the island, and centuries' old individuals of great beauty may be seen at the entrance to the Samaria gorge. Cypresses are also found in the Imbros gorge and in the ravines near the sea. On the White Mountains, the cypress cohabits with *Acer sempervirens* and *Quercus coccifera*.

PINUS BRUTIA TEN. 33
(Pinaceae)

Growing to 30 meters height with a straight trunk, this member of the Pine family has needle-like leaves 8 to 12 cm in length and slightly curved cones. It is found at altitudes of up to 1200 meters on rocky soils, on the accumulated detritus in the gorges, and on the calcareous slopes. It sometimes forms extensive populations, above all in the White Mountains, the Sitía range and on Mount Díkti. These are natural forests, even though they must be considered replacements of the original forests, and are habitats of priority interest. From this and other species of pine is derived a substance used for flavoring and preserving the dry white wine called *retsina* often found on Greek tables. *Pinus brutia* is not attacked by grazing animals due to its pungent flavor, but since it contains resin, it burns easily. On the other hand, the periods following fires are those in which the plant propagates most rapidly: the mature cones, in fact, explode in the heat and launch their seeds to great distances, thus guaranteeing the spread of the species. This pine is found growing on arid substrates above all in areas well-exposed to the sun. In the pine forests we find only few herbaceous plants, mainly orchids.

33

ACER SEMPERVIRENS **L.** 34
(Aceraceae)

This evergreen member of the Maple family grows on rocky slopes and in open woodlands on calcareous soils from 200 to 1700 meters above sea level. It may reach 5 meters in height; the leaves are obscurely or more frequently shallowly three-lobed. Flowers in April and May; when the blossoms fall, the winged fruits (samaras) appear grouped in lax racemes.

CYCLAMEN CRETICUM (**DORFL.**) **HILDEBR.** 35
(Primulaceae)

The white flowers of this beautiful cyclamen, endemic to Crete and often called the Cretan Sowbread, can be seen in the spring in the cypress or pine woods, in the maquis, and in shady rocky areas at altitudes of up to 100 meters.
The form and color of the leaves recall those of ivy; they are borne on long pinkish-brown petioles and have toothed margins. The fragrant flowers are white, with typically long, narrow petals. The tuber is rather large, with a flattened tip.

In past years, this cyclamen was indiscriminately gathered by plant nurseries; today, the species is included in Appendix II of the Convention on International Trade in Endangered Species of Wild Fauna and Flora (CITES).

ARUM IDAEUM **COUSTUR. & GAND.** 36
(Araceae)

Endemic to the island of Crete, this perennial lives in the mountainous areas from 900 to 2400 meters altitude, on rocky calcareous soils and often in association with *Berberis cretica*. The unisexual flowers are borne along a fleshy stalk called a spadix, with the male flowers above and the female below. The spadix is sheathed in a covering, the spathe, which is 5 to 8 cm in length with a clearly defined constriction at about mid-length; it is white with purplish veins inside and a green blush outside. The fruits are berries; the leaves are shiny green and long-stalked.

34

35

37

SELAGINELLA DENTICULATA (L.) SPRING [37]
(Selaginellaceae)

A small, low fern with short, delicate pale green, creeping stems. The leaves are set out in four rows: those of the outer two are broader and flatter than those above, which are smaller are appressed to the branched stems. All the leaves are oval, finely toothed, entire, and no longer than 2.5 mm. The Mediterranean Selaginella reproduces by spores, which are borne in special tiny organs called sporangia.

38

39

PYRUS SPINOSA FORSSK. [38] [39]
(Rosaceae)

The Almond-Leaved Pear, so-called due to the resemblance of its leaves to those of the almond, is a deciduous shrub or small tree, often densely branched and sometimes spiny. The leaves are narrowly elliptical, entire or with three shallowly-cut lobes. Flowers in March and April; the flowers have five white petals that are blunted at the apex. The globose fruit, from yellow to brown in color, bears the dried sepals of the calyx at its top.

MAQUIS

Following intensive exploitation and firing of the woodlands, the trees give way to shrubs and small evergreen sclerophylls, growing to 5 to 7 meters, that form closed, compact, often impenetrable biocenoses called maquis. The term *maquis*, Corsican in origin, derives from the Latin *macula* (spot) and alludes to the differences in color and the irregular distribution of the plants in this type of vegetation formation. In truth, the meaning of the term would make it better suited to describing the garrigue, as we will see further on.

On Crete, the maquis is well-developed up to about 1100 meters altitude and above all in the western part of the island where the climate is more humid, but it often appears in degraded forms as a consequence of fires and grazing. Characteristic elements of the maquis, especially near the coasts, are the Olive, the Carob, the Kermes Oak, the Phoenician Juniper, and, where the light is stronger, *Styrax officinalis*.

There are a number of different types of maquis, like the scrub maquis with *Euphorbia dendroides* in the rupestrian areas, the tall maquis with *Pistacia lentiscus*, and the Olive-Carob maquis, where many elements typical of the garrigues may be found: *Calycotome villosa*, *Cistus salviifolius*, *Genista acanthoclada*, and, in the damper areas, *Laurus nobilis* and *Myrtus communis*.

The Olive-Lentisc maquis, with Carob and Myrtle, is a habitat of naturalistic interest at the Community level.

Different types of maquis formations. Top, Kermes Oak; center, a highly-degraded maquis; bottom, Euphorbia dendroides.

LAURUS NOBILIS **L.** 46
(Lauraceae)

Mythology tells us that the Laurel or Sweet Bay plant originated when Daphne, the nymph loved by Apollo, was transformed into a laurel tree. It has always been considered a symbol of victory, respect, and power: Apollo himself encircled his head with a crown of laurel when he entered Delphi victorious; the Pythia, before delivering her oracles, chewed the leaves of the plant. In more recent times, the crown of plaited laurel branches adorned the heads of young graduates. The curative and aromatic properties of the plant have also been known and appreciated since antiquity: *Oleum lauri* or Oil of Bay, an ingredient of unguents for alleviating rheumatic pains, is obtained from the fruits, and the leaves have always been used as in seasoning food and as an aroma per liquors.

The leaves of this evergreen shrub are alternate, lanceolate, and aromatic; the yellow flowers appear in March and April and produce black fruits. On Crete, *Laurus nobilis* L. is found in the central and western regions, at low altitudes. It

46

is frequently used as an ornamental plant in gardens, above all for creating hedges that are often pruned in artistic forms.

MYRTUS COMMUNIS **L.** SUBSP. *COMMUNIS* 47
(Myrtaceae)

This plant was sacred to Aphrodite, who used its branches to cover her nudity when she emerged from the sea; the myrtle has also always been considered a symbol of beauty and youth. In ancient times, the Common Myrtle was considered a medicinal plant, a panacea for all ills and a valid antidote for the poisons of spiders and scorpions. It was used medicinally, and in particular as an expectorant and disinfectant for the respiratory tract; today, the leaves and fruits are used mainly for flavoring liquors and for seasoning fish dishes. The leaves are opposite and decussate, pointed, shiny and highly aromatic due to the aromatic oils they contain. The flowers are formed of five white petals, five sepals and a great number of stamens. The fruit is a small oval berry, dark blue in color, that bears the dried calyx at its top. On Crete, the myrtle is found in the western and central portions of the island.

47

GARRIGUE AND PHRYGANA

We have stressed how, following human exploitation of the woodlands, fires, and grazing, the maquis vegetation suffers a gradual degradation: the impoverishment of the soil thus bared and erosion phenomena make life difficult for the trees and the taller shrubs. The maquis is thus replaced, especially where

The phrygana (top) may be considered a degraded form of maquis (bottom).

aridity is greatest, by the garrigue and phrygana formations. The first is composed of evergreen shrubs and suffruticose plants (subshrubs) 50 to 100 cm tall, while the latter is formed of shrubs up to 50 cm, generally with summer-deciduous leaves. In practice it is not always easy to make a clear distinction between the two types of vegetation, since there exist many intermediate formations and since many plants are common to both habitats. In both these vegetation formations we find plants typical of the lands facing on the Aegean Sea; the species described below are those that characterize each formation and those that differentiate among them.

GARRIGUE

The garrigues are discontinuous vegetation formations on land with protruding rocks, with wide-open spaces between plants; they are characterized by sclerophyllous shrubs and subshrubs, growing to a maximum of one meter, that are frequently spiny and graze-resistant. The garrigues are found both near the sea and in the interior; the components vary according to the substrate, the altitude, and the phytogeographical area. There exist different types of garrigues dominated by different plants: those characterized by *Euphorbia acanthoclada*, by *Phlomis fruticosa*, and by *Salvia fruticosa* are all considered habitats of Community interest. Among the most common garrigue elements are various representatives of the genus *Cistus*, with their beautiful although ephemeral flowers and their enviable capacity to recover rapidly following fires, *Daphne sericea* and *Lavandula stoechas*, with their strongly-perfumed flowers, and *Calycotome villosa*, a spiny shrub with yellow flowers. In the open spaces we find myriad herbaceous plants, the Common Asphodel and the Yellow Asphodel, and many bulbous plants including the showy orchids of the genera *Ophrys* and *Orchis*. The damper areas are preferred by three plants of the family Scrophulariaceae (*Bellardia trixago*, *Parentucellia latifolia*, and *P. viscosa*) and the orchids of the genus *Serapias*.

The garrigue in full flower; the pink blossoms of the Rockroses stand out among the many plants.

CISTUS CRETICUS L. [48]
(Cistaceae)

This member of the Rockrose family is characterized by its showy flowers and the copious white hairs on the undersurface of the leaves. It is a densely-branched shrub with opposite, oval-lanceolate leaves with slightly wavy margins. The flowers (March through May), 4 to 6 cm in diameter, solitary or in groups of 2 to 3, have 5 sepals and 5 ephemeral petals; the basal portion of the bright pink petal is yellow, as are the numerous stamens. The plant provides a resin used in medicine and perfume-making; in the Middle Ages, the monks gathered the resin using special rakes, which they passed over the plants in the warmest hours of the day, when the resin is exuded like dewdrops.

CISTUS PARVIFLORUS LAM. [49]
(Cistaceae)

This 'small-flowered' Cistus is a densely-branched shrub that grows to 70 cm, with undulate leaves that are slightly tomentous on the

48

upper surface. The many pink flowers, at most 3 cm in diameter, appear in April and May. Like the other Rockroses, this species is a pyrophyte, and the scattering of its seeds is favored by fire. This eastern Mediterranean element thrives in the garrigues but also in the phrygana formations and in open conifer woods.

CISTUS SALVIIFOLIUS L. [51]
(Cistaceae)

Similar, but with large white flowers 4 to 5 cm in diameter. The greenish-grey leaves of the aptly-called Sage-Leaved Cistus are opposite, not sticky, and hairy on the undersurface, similarly to those of common sage; hence the species name.

CYTINUS HYPOCISTIS (L.) L. [50]
(Rafflesiaceae)

A quite peculiar plant, which since it possesses no photosynthetic organs lives as a parasite on various species of the genus *Cistus*. The stem is short, sometimes fleshy, and covered with fleshy scalelike leaves that are yellow toward the base of the plant and red higher on the stem. The leaves envelop the flowers, which are formed of four

49

yellow or white tepals; the center flowers are male and the outer flowers are female. The fruit is a berry that in ancient times was pressed to obtain a juice used as a cure for stomach pains. There are two subspecies on Crete, *Cytinus hypocistis* (L.) L. subsp. *clusii* Nyman and *Cytinus hypocistis* (L.)

L. subsp. *hypocistis*. Both subspecies, which are quite similar, are rare and live in the same environments; they differ as to the species of *Cistus* on which they are parasitic (*Cistus creticus* the former, *C. parviflorus* and *C. salviifolius* the latter).

50

51

52

PHLOMIS FRUTICOSA L. 52 54
(Labiatae)

The so-called Jerusalem Sage is a densely-hairy shrub growing as tall as 1.3 meters. The light green leaves are wrinkly on the upper surface and white-felted beneath. The basal leaves are lanceolate or elliptical, with petioles, and are 3 to 9 cm in length; the cauline leaves are sessile. The flowers appear from April through June in groups of 20 to 30 in terminal verticillasters with pointed bracteoles covered with stellate hairs; the two-lipped corolla is yellow; the calyx has hooked teeth and stellate hairs. This plant lives in the garrigues, on calcareous soils from sea level to 1050 meters, above all in central and western Crete.

53

54

CALICOTOME VILLOSA (POIR.) LINK [53]
(Leguminosae)

An evergreen shrub that, as the species name suggests, is hairy in all its parts: the leaves, the young branches, the calyx, and the fruits. The branches bear sharp stout spines and alternate leaves composed of three small, hairy leaflets. The flowers have a yellow papilionaceous corolla and are grouped in glomerules that appear in March and April. The plant can be found from sea level to 1600 meters altitude; it also thrives in the phrygana and in the maquis and may form extensive populations.

SALVIA FRUTICOSA MILL. [55]
(Labiatae)

The old name of this plant was *Salvia triloba*; in fact, the leaves are generally trilobate, with the central lobe being much larger than the lateral lobes. It is a shrub growing to 1.5 meters, covered with a dense whitish tomentum. The flowers are grouped in more or less crowded verticils; they are pink tending to various degrees to white. Flowers from March through May. *S. fruticosa* Mill. is widely distributed throughout the entire island of Crete.

55

61

62

ASPARAGUS APHYLLUS L. SUBSP. ORIENTALIS (BAKER) P.H. DAVIS [63]
(Liliaceae)

A plant with stout white or grey stems up to 2 meters, with lighter-colored longitudinal striations. The leaves are no more than small scales and the photosynthetic function is performed by reduced stems called cladodes, of different lengths but all spine-tipped, that are grouped in clusters of 10 to 30. Flowers in October; the flowers are white and the fruits are black berries.

ANTHYLLIS VULNERARIA L. SUBSP. RUBRIFLORA (DC.) ARCANG. [61]
(Leguminosae)

A perennial with erect, ascending, hairy stems. The lower leaves are composed of a single leaflet, while the leaves higher on the stem are compound with 7 to 13 elliptical leaflets. The purple-red flowers are borne in flowerheads covered with bracts; the shiny calyxes, with their silky hairs, are purple at the tips. Flowers from March through July. This plant is found in fields and in rocky areas as well as in the garrigues. The species name refers to the vulnerary properties of the flowers, which were dried and used as a balm for contusions and wounds.

63

FUMANA ARABICA (L.) SPACH [62]
(Cistaceae)

A small bushy plant with prostrate or erect stems that grow to a maximum length of 25 cm. The green-grey leaves are alternate, ovate-lanceolate, flat, and pointed. The flowers, solitary or grouped in cymes of up to 7 in number, are yellow with a darker spot at the base. The plant, which is frequently found in the maquis as well as in the garrigue and phrygana formations, flowers between March and May.

64

BELLARDIA TRIXAGO (L.) ALL. [64]
(Scrophulariaceae)

An erect semi-parasitic annual up to 30 cm, with stiff, branched, glandular-hairy stems. The leaves are opposite, linear-lanceolate, saw-toothed, and covered, like the stems, with glandular hairs. The flowers, with white corollas and a yellow or pink lip, appear from March through June in dense four-sided spike inflorescences.

PARENTUCELLIA VISCOSA (L.) CARUEL IN PARL. [65]
(*Scrophulariaceae*)

A glandular, viscous semi-parasitic annual growing to 40 cm, with erect, green branches and sessile, lanceolate leaves. The flowers are generally yellow, although occasionally white or purple, and are grouped in dense spike inflorescences no longer than 8 cm. Flowers from March through June in shady positions on rocky soils.

PARENTUCELLIA LATIFOLIA (L.) CARUEL IN PARL. [66]
(*Scrophulariaceae*)

Another semi-parasitic annual, at most 20 cm tall but often lower; it is glandular, with a generally reddish stem bearing opposite leaves with toothed margins. The flowers are purple-red and appear from March through May in small inflorescences. This plant prefers rocky soils but may also be found growing in abandoned fields and grassy habitats, often near the coast.

65

66

brown or purple longitudinal stripe. The leaves are linear-lanceolate. This perennial is found above all in the central and western portions of the island, where it lives in the garrigue and phrygana environments; it is also found on the calcareous cliffs in the crevices of the rock, from sea level to 400 meters.

an equally curious aspect at flowering time (April and May): the first thing we notice are the many stamens and the five fused styles over the ring of small blue nectaries and the sky-blue tepals, which are subtended by threadlike bracts. The fruit is also quite showy: it is a globose capsule of membranous consistency and green in color with red veinings; at maturity, the limbs of the capsule spread at the apex to release the many tiny seeds. This plant is often gathered at the moment of fructification for use is used in dry flower arrangements.

GAGEA GRAECA (L.) A. TERRACC. [67]
(*Liliaceae*)

The tepals, up to 15 mm in length, are white with a somewhat marked

NIGELLA DAMASCENA L. [68]
(*Ranunculaceae*)

This plant, with the curious common English name of Love-in-a-Mist, has

67

68

69

IRIS UNGUICULARIS
POIR. SUBSP. _CRETENSIS_ (JANKA) A.P. DAVIS & JURY [69]
(Iridaceae)

The Algerian Iris, growing from 10 to 50 cm tall, vaunts beautiful flowers in the period February-May: the perianth tube of the flower may be as long as 20 cm; the tepals are an intense violet color and very fragrant. At the base of the external tepals, which are turned downward, is a vivid orange spot with a white band; the internal tepals are erect. The style is branched and glandular. This iris grows on rocky slopes and in the phrygana at altitudes from sea level to that of the submontane plain.

OROBANCHE RAMOSA L. SUBSP. _MUTELII_ (F.W. SCHULTZ) COUT. [70]
(Orobanchaceae)

A small parasitic plant possessing no leaves and therefore forced to exploit other plants (above all of the species *Solanum* and the family Leguminosae) to obtain carbohydrates. The perennate parts of the plant are underground; all we see is the inflorescence, which is composed of an erect, branched stalk, covered with thick glandular down, bearing many blue flowers, each 15 to 22 cm long and subtended by three bracts. Flowering time lasts through the summer.

70

PHRYGANA

The phrygana, or Oriental spiny garrigue, is an advanced stage in the degradation of the maquis following deforestation, intensive grazing and fire. Differently from the garrigue, it is dominated by hemispherical shrubs, at most 50 cm tall, that are generally spiny and aromatic and intricately and compactly branched; the leaves are in most cases caducous in summer and are graze- and drought-resistant. In this type of formation, like in the garrigue, the shrubs grow at a distance the ones from the others, leaving broad expanses of bare rock.

*Rockroses in flower in the phrygana
in a coastal area.*

The phrygana formations are commonly distributed throughout the entire eastern Mediterranean, where they cover extensive surfaces in areas marked by strong aridity, above all near the coasts, forming a belt between the cliff-dwelling plant communities and the thermomediterranean shrub formations in the interior. The phrygana formation found in the countries on the Aegean Sea is a Community-interest habitat formed of *Sarcopoterium spinosum, Satureja thymbra, Coridothymus capitatus, Genista acanthoclada, Euphorbia acanthothamnos, Ballota acetabulosa, Fumana arabica* and *F. thymifolia, Cistus creticus, C. parviflorus* and *C. salviifolius, Pistacia lentiscus, Teucrium brevifolium, Calycotome villosa,*

Salvia fruticosa, and *Phagnalon graecum.*
On Crete, this type of formation occupies a wide strip of territory, and the mid-altitude phrygana, in contact with the lower-lying phrygana formation and the area characterized by spiny bushes, is a habitat of Community interest that counts *Euphorbia acanthothamnos , Berberis cretica, Hypericum empetrifolium,* and *Genista acanthoclada* among its distinctive elements.

The hemispherical cushions of Euphorbia acanthothamnos (below and bottom right) and the showy orchids (top right) are typical of the phrygana formations. Facing page: the coastal phrygana near Sitía.

On Crete there exist various types of phrygana in relation to the dominant shrubs; the three dominated by *Sarcopoterium spinosum* (the most widespread), by *Genista acanthoclada,* and by *Coridothymus capitatus,* respectively, are habitats of Community interest.
There are also many herbaceous plants in the phrygana, such as *Cyclamen creticum, Bellardia trixago,* species of the Milkwort family (Polygalaceae), *Centaurea raphanina, Tragopogon sinuatus, Asphodelus aestivus, Asphodeline lutea, Gynandiris sisyrinchium, Dracunculus vulgaris,* and, less frequently, *Aristolochia cretica* and *Onosma erectum.* There are also many orchids, primarily members of the genera *Ophrys* and *Orchis.*

SARCOPOTERIUM SPINOSUM (**L.**) **SPACH** [71]
(Rosaceae)

One of the most typical components of the phrygana is this small spiny shrub that forms dense and intricate bushes about 50 cm tall. The leaves, which are composed of 9 to 15 small segments, have toothed margins and are tomentose on the underside; they fall at the beginning of the summer season. The flowers are grouped in elongated inflorescences containing both male and female, above and below respectively. The small round fruits change color from red to brown upon ripening.

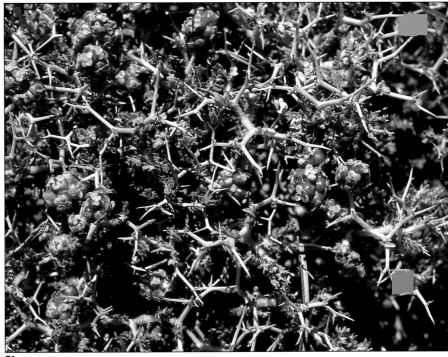

71

78

79

BALLOTA ACETABULOSA L. (BENTH.) 78
(Labiatae)

A perennial growing to 50 cm, covered with a dense, silky down; the numerous erect stems are woody at the base and bear opposite leaves with heart-shaped bases and crenelated margins. Flowers purple and white; the distinguishing feature of this plant is its calyx, formed of a wide funnel-shaped membranous wing. Still today, the calyxes are dried and used as wicks for oil lamps. This plant is found mainly in the western portion of Crete.

FUMANA THYMIFOLIA (L.)SPACH EX WEBB 79
(Cistaceae)

A small, branched shrub to 20 cm, with erect or prostrate stems. The leaves are small and linear,

with revolute margins. The yellow flowers, occasionally with a reddish spot at the base of each petal, are borne in apical inflorescences of 3 to 9 flowers each. Flowers from March through May. Lives in arid habitats and in the wooded areas.

TEUCRIUM BREVIFOLIUM SCHREB. 80
(Labiatae)

This shrub, with its intricately-woven, greyish or brown pubescent branches, grows to 60 cm. The leaves are oblong or linear, with decidedly revolute margins. The flowers, visible in March and April, are irregular with insignificant upper lip and a well-developed lower lip divided into five sky-blue lobes. *T. brevifolium* Schreb. is found in rocky areas, both in the garrigue and the phrygana formations.

PHAGNALON GRAECUM BOISS. & HELDR. IN BOISS. 81
(Compositae)

The erect, white-woolly stems of this species grow no taller than 50 cm. The elongated oval leaves, glabrous above and densely white-felted on the underside, are undulate with revolute margins. The solitary yellow flowerheads are enclosed by dark-colored, sometimes hairy, closely overlapping membranous bracts. Flowers in April and May.

80

81

HYPERICUM EMPETRIFOLIUM WILLD. 82
(Guttiferae)

The rocky terrains are often brightened by the vivacious note of color lent by this small shrub, which in April and May is covered with a myriad of yellow flowers with long, narrow petals.
The sepals are much shorter than the petals and are marked by small dark glands that are visible even to the naked eye. The glabrous, linear leaves are grouped in verticils of three.
This species has been known since antiquity and prized as a remedy for wounds.
A similar species, *H. amblycalyx* Coustur. & Gand., is endemic to Crete, where it lives on the rocks; it differs from *H. empetrifolium* as regards its leaves, which are grouped in verticils of four, and its glandless sepals.

BERBERIS CRETICA L. 83
(Berberidaceae)

This shrub lives at altitudes of between 900 and 2200 meters on the rocky calcareous soils of the White Mountains and on Mounts Díkti and Afendis Kavoussi. Its deciduous leaves are unlobed, clustered, and subtended by tripartite spines. The flowers are yellow and the fruits are dark red, oblong berries.

ANTHYLLIS HERMANNIAE L. 84
(Leguminosae)

A shrub to 50 cm, with contorted, spine-tipped branches. The lower leaves are simple, while those above are composed of three narrow, hairy leaflets. The flowers, up to one centimeter long, are found singly or in clusters of 2 to 3 at the leaf-axils. The distinctive feature of this shrub, which is otherwise easily mistaken for a gorse or a broom, is that the tube of the corolla is narrow and elongated and the calyx has five equal teeth instead of being two-lipped. It is found, besides in the phrygana, in the *Pinus brutia* woodlands and on the coasts, in association with *Juniperus phoenicea* and *Thymelaea hirsuta*.

82

83

85

86

87

POLYGALA MONSPELIACA L. [87]
(*Polygalaceae*)

The hermaphrodite flowers of the Milkworts are quite distinctive: of the five separate sepals, two (wings), are longer than the other three; two petals are fused at the base to form a tube called the carina, and the lower petal is fringed at the apex.
P. monspeliaca L. is an annual, with lanceolate leaves up to 25 mm in length. The flowers (March-April) are grouped in terminal racemes and are formed of whitish wings with blue or green veinings, and white petals. This relatively rare plant lives in the phrygana from 100 to 400 meters above sea level.

POLYGALA VENULOSA SM. [85]
(*Polygalaceae*)

Another comparatively rare species that is found in the phrygana and in the shrub-covered areas from sea level to 1200 meters altitude. The flowers are blue, with the wings very much shorter than the petals. Differently from the other Milkworts, *P. venulosa* Sm. is a perennial.

GYNANDRIRIS SISYRINCHIUM (L.) PARL. [86]
(*Iridaceae*)

This beautiful small plant is found from sea level to altitudes of 700 meters, where it lives not only in the phrygana but also on field margins and on rocky and sandy coastlines. The flowers appear from March through May, but are very short-lived, opening at midday and withering in the evening. The blue or violet tepals, with a white spot and a smaller orange spot in the basal portion, are 3 cm in length. The species name derives from the Greek *gyne* (female) and *andros* (male), after the stamens that adhere tightly to the ramification of the style. The leaves, one or two in number, are less than one cm in width, downward-curving, and provided with a long sheath that curls when dry. The bulb is almost spherical and is enveloped in light-colored fibers.

RANUNCULUS ASIATICUS L. [88]
(*Ranunculaceae*)

This beautiful herbaceous perennial Buttercup, 10 to 40 cm in height, is bristly-hairy all over and otherwise highly variable. The leaves of the basal rosette are orbiculate and crenate, with long petioles and three wide and rather deeply-incised lobes; the lobes of the upper leaves are instead linear. The caulis is simple or branched above and bears from 1 to 4 flowers, each 2 to 8 cm in diameter. The flowers are generally white or slightly pinkish; truly pink-flowered individuals are found sporadically, and red-flowered individuals are even rarer. The plant flowers from March through May on the rocky soil of the phrygana, but it may also be found in cultivated or abandoned fields and along roadsides.

89

HELICHRYSUM BARRELIERI (TEN.) GREUTER 89
(Compositae)

The aroma of this species is much more tenuous than that of other members of the genus *Helichrysum*. The broad linear or spatulate tomentous leaves are less than 20 mm in length. The yellow flowers, all tubular and grouped in compact flowerheads, and may be seen from April through June. *H. barrelieri* can also be found in exposed sandy coastal habitats.

*

Spring in the phrygana sees the flowering of many orchids. Given the peculiar form of the flowers of the plants of the members of the Orchid family, the descriptions of the single species are preceded by brief notes about orchids in general and about the genera *Orchis*,

Ophrys, and *Serapias* in particular.
The orchids are perennial plants that generally grow from a pair of bulbs or rounded tubers; the leaves are entire, with parallel venation; the stem is simple and the inflorescence is a more or less compact spike or raceme. The irregular flowers are always accompanied by green or colored bracts and are formed of 6 tepals arranged in 2 verticils of 3 tepals each. Of the three external tepals, that at the center generally differs from the others; on the inner whorl, the two outside tepals are smaller and the central tepal, called the labellum, is always showy as to both form and color and may in turn be subdivided into lobes and bear a spur of varying form. Another peculiar feature of these plants is the fact that the flowers are resupinate; that is, turned upside-down due to torsion of the peduncle, in such a manner that the labellum is always downwards, while its normal position would be at

the top of the flower. The stamens and pistils are fused in a peculiar structure called a gynostemium, and the pollen is aggregated into small masses called pollinia. The fruit is a capsule containing many tiny seeds that in order to germinate must be infected by a fungus with which the plant later establishes a symbiotic relationship. The size, form, and coloration of the flowers are highly variable among the different species of orchids. Thanks to their showy and highly distinctive flowers, the orchids are the plants which perhaps arouse the most curiosity. But it must always be remembered that many of the species are rare and often distributed only in limited geographical areas - and for this reason are protected by law: all the species described in this guide are included in Appendix II to the Convention on International Trade in Endangered Species of Wild Fauna and Flora (CITES).

ACERAS ANTHROPOPHORUM (L.) W.T. AITON 90
(Orchidaceae)

The species name of this orchid derives from the form of the labellum, which is divided into two lateral lobes and one central lobe, which is in turn again divided so that it resembles a tiny man with long arms and legs (from the Greek *anthropos* = man, and *fero* = carry). Five greenish segments form a sort of helmet or hood above the brown-red labellum. The flowers of the Man Orchid are grouped in a spike up to 20 cm in length. The leaves may be as long as 12 cm.

ANACAMPTIS PYRAMIDALIS (L.) RICH. 91
(Orchidaceae)

This orchid, growing from 20 to 60 cm, has 4 to 10 leaves, the lower being erect and the upper much reduced. The pink flowers, grouped in a pyramidal inflorescence, have a decidedly three-lobed labellum, small internal tepals, concave external tepals, and a long, very slender spur. Flowers in April and May.

*

The genus *Ophrys* counts the most spectacular of the orchids, since the forms, the colors, and the surface tex-

90

tures of the labella resemble those of the female of the species of insects that performs pollination of each orchid. The male insect (whether honeybee, wasp, hornet, or bumblebee) is attracted by the look of the flower and certain substances it emits, similar to those produced by the female as a mating call. The insect lands on the labellum, where it comes into contact with the pollinia; these attach to its body until it performs pollination when it visits another flower. The inflorescences of the genus *Ophrys* are generally formed of only a few flowers. The tepals are usually not very conspicuous, to the exception of the entire or three-lobed labellum, which is convex or gibbous and either glabrous or hairy with a shiny central area of varying form and color. This 'speculum' is always glabrous and as such useful for species identification.

91

OPHRYS IRICOLOR DESF. 92
(Orchidaceae)

An orchid growing to from 15 to 30 cm, with an inflorescence composed of one to 5 large flowers. The brown outer tepals are linear, about 15 mm long, rounded or truncated at the apex, and somewhat undulated. The dark brown labellum is flat, 15 to 22 mm long, and densely villous, with three wide lobes tapering toward the base; the speculum is a metallic, iridescent blue, hence the species name. Flowers in March and April.

OPHRYS SPHEGODES MILL. SUBSP. CRETENSIS H. BAUMANN & KUNKELE 93
(Orchidaceae)

Ten to 45 centimeters in height, with mucronate, ovate-lanceolate leaves. The flowers (March-April) are grouped in 2 to 20 lax inflorescences. The external tepals are green flushed whitish or reddish; the dorsal tepal is erect or bent forward. The inner tepals are 4 to 8 mm in length. The orbiculate labellum is velvety, and brown-red or black in color, with a brilliant blue speculum more or less closely resembling the letter H, sometimes narrowly edged in white; the labellum may have a small yellow appendage below. There is another subspecies of this orchid on Crete, endemic to the island: the subspecies *gortynia* H. Baumann & Kunkele differs from the subspecies *cretensis* described above in its later flowering period and the cuneiform base of its labellum.

92

93

94

OPHRYS HOLOSERICA (BURM. F.) GREUTER SUBSP. MAXIMA (H. FLEISCHM.) GREUTER 94
(Orchidaceae)

This orchid is 20 to 40 cm tall, with 4 to 10 large flowers. The external tepals are dark red with green veining at the center. The almost rectangular labellum is velvety and reddish-brown, with a center spot in the form of a very broad H from which there diverge two yellow motifs in the form of more or less accentuated pendents; the labellum terminates in a denticulate yellow appendage. This orchid can be found up to 1200 meters altitude, in the phrygana as well as in the pine woods and abandoned terraced fields.

OPHRYS LUTEA CAV. SUBSP. MINOR (TOD.) O. & E. DANESCH 95 96
(Orchidaceae)

The flowers of this orchid, which grows to from 5 to 40 cm in height, are borne in groups of 3 to 8. The labellum, 8 to 13 mm in length, is short-hairy and grey tending to violet or brownish; it becomes purple-brown or blackish toward the terminal portion. Flowers from January through April in the garrigue and the phrygana; also found in woods and olive groves.

*

The flowers of the plants in the genus *Orchis* are formed of external and inner tepals that generally converge in a helmet-shaped structure. The labellum may be straight or slightly curved, entire or three-lobed, and glabrous or dotted with small papillae.

95

96

97

ORCHIS QUADRIPUNCTATA CIRILLO EX TEN. [97]
(Orchidaceae)

This orchid grows to from 10 to 30 cm on a thick stem flushed red above. The flowers (March-May) are from pink to purple in color and grouped in a lax cylindrical inflorescence; the external tepals are slightly back-curving; the labellum is three-lobed, with at its center a light colored spot and generally four dark spots in the middle near the top, a slightly convex median lobe, and a cylindrical spur up to 14 mm long. This species lives in the pockets of earth among the rocks and may also be found in the gorges and pine woods.

ORCHIS CORIOPHORA L. SUBSP. *FRAGRANS* (POLLINI) SUDRE [98]
(Orchidaceae)

The basal leaves of this orchid are narrow and the cauline leaves sheathe the stem almost completely. The flowers (April-June) are rather small and quite numerous, from 20 to 40, with an acuminate purplish-red or greenish helmet; the labellum is divided into 3 papillate lobes that may be purple or brown with dark spots at the base; the median lobe is longer than the others. This is a very variable orchid as regards the size of the stem, the color, and the form of the labellum and the spur.

98

99

100

ORCHIS BORYI RCHB. F. 99 100
(Orchidaceae)

This orchid is found only on Crete and in southern Greece. The stem rises to from 20 to 45 cm from a globose tuber. The flowers appear from March through May in a lax inflorescence. The external tepals are intense violet in color; the suborbiculate labellum is 8 by 8 mm, with 3 more or less equal lobes, and pink in color with a lighter-colored spot at the center that is in turn dotted with small, darker spots; the threadlike spur is 15 mm in length and distended or upward-curving.

ORCHIS LACTEA POIR. IN LAM. 101
(Orchidaceae)

The stem is 7 to 20 cm long. The white or greenish-pink flowers (February-April) are grouped in an ovoid inflorescence. The labellum has three deeply-cut, linear lobes and one central orbicular-obovate or spatulate lobe that is toothed at the apex; it is cream-colored spotted with purple; the lateral lobes are obliquely truncated. The spur is somewhat longer than the ovary.

ORCHIS TRIDENTATA SCOP. 103
(Orchidaceae)

A rather rare orchid, and one of great beauty. It is 25 to 50 centimeters in height, with flowers (March-April) grouped in a conical inflorescence. The external tepals are long-pointed and their tips often diverge; the labellum is three-lobed with truncated, toothed apices; the median lobe is slightly bilobate and pink with darker margins and spots near the center. The spur is circular in section and downcurved.

ORCHIS PAUCIFLORA TEN. 102
(Orchidaceae)

The stem is 15 to 35 cm tall. The flowers (March-April) are relatively large and form lax spikes of only 3 to 7 flowers each; the external and internal tepals and

101

the spur are light yellow;
the labellum, bright yellow with
tiny purple spots at the center, has
an orbiculate-truncated center
lobe folding from the center-line
or convex, with an irregularly-
toothed margin; the spur is
cylindrical.

102

103

04

105

ORCHIS ANATOLICA BOISS. SUBSP. SITIACA RENZ. 104 105
(Orchidaceae)

An orchid having a lax inflorescence of 2 to 15 flowers with narrow pink external tepals with a green blush; the trilobate labellum is sharply bent; the lateral lobes lie under the median lobe, which is truncated and s scarcely divided with a lighter-colored spot at the center and darker dots. The spur is about 20 mm in length. *Orchis anatolica* is distributed on the islands of the eastern Aegean, while *Orchis anatolica* subsp. *sitiaca* is endemic to Crete, where it can be found in the central and eastern portions of the island.

*

In the plants of the genus *Serapias*, the leaves are narrow, pointed, and generally a beautiful brilliant green. The bracts are the same color as the flowers, which are composed of pointed or lanceolate outer tepals that with the internal tepals form a distinctive pointed helmet formation. The wide labellum is composed of a basal portion, called the hypochilium, with two indistinct lateral lobes, and a well-developed apical portion, called the epichilium, that is typically pendent and quite prominent. Identification of the members of the genus *Serapias* may be complicated by the considerable degree of variability that marks even the single species, and by their tendency to hybridize. The genus name recalls Serapias, the Egyptian god of fertility.

106

SERAPIAS BERGONII E.G. CAMUS 106
(Orchidaceae)

Ten to 55 cm in height, often with a reddish blush on the base

of the stem and the leaves. The inflorescence groups 3 to 12 flowers (March-May). The obliquely-set helmet is lavender-gray; the labellum is light red or purple and the hypochilium pinkish ochre with short white hairs. The lateral lobes of the labellum are dark purple and are hidden inside the helmet. This is a rather variable orchid.

SERAPIAS ORIENTALIS (GREUTER) H. BAUMANN & KUNKELE SUBSP. ORIENTALIS 107
(Orchidaceae)

Ten to 30 cm in height, with flowers (March-May) grouped in a short, rather dense spike. The helmet is pinkish-grey with greenish or lavender veins. The outer tepals are 20 to 32 mm long and slightly keeled; the labellum is 28 to 40 mm in length and ochre, deep pink, or purple in color and white-hairy in the median portion. May also be found in pine woods and in fields.

107

THE RUPESTRIAN HABITATS: CLIFFS, DETRITUS, ROCKY SOILS

The cliffs are a difficult environment for plant life: the strong winds, the exiguity of the soil layer, and the slope of the land join with the marked swings between daytime and nighttime temperatures to create conditions of aridity and little available nutrients and space. In such conditions only highly specialized plants can survive: these are the chasmophytes, plants that colonize the cracks and crevices in the rock. Certain species live exclusively on vertical cliffs, while others may be found on non-vertical rock walls as well. Due to the intrinsic conditions of the environments in which they live, the chasmophytes almost never form extensive populations. Many are perennials, and small in size; they sometimes take on a cushion-like form. They constitute a type of vegetation that remains quite stable over time thanks to the lack of competition from other plants and the very inaccessibility of their habitats, which effectively subtracts them from the risks posed by grazing and human meddling.

Certain of the cliff-dwelling plants are extremely beautiful: the showiest are far and away *Petromarula pinnata*, with its elongated inflorescences of blossoms varying in color from blue to violet, and *Ebenus cretica*, which forms spreading bushes with dense pink inflorescences; both these plants are endemic to Crete and are widely distributed and easy to see just about anywhere on the island. Another typical plant is *Inula candida*, which owes its name to the dense white down that covers all its parts; this adaptation is of particular importance in reducing transpiration. Other cliff-dwelling species include *Linum arboreum*, with its yellow flowers, *Aethionema saxatile*, with its small round inflorescences of many flowers, and many species of *Campanula*.

The cliffs have no fixed altitudinal reference, since they are found from sea level to the highest mountain peaks. They do represent a very interesting habitat from the botanical point of view, and are included among the habitats of Community interest. This is the case, in particular, of the cliffs of Crete populated by *Petromarula pinnata*, *Ebenus creticus*, *Inula candida*, and various species of *Campanula*.

The flowers of the cliffs are without doubt very interesting formations, and during a stay on Crete can be seen frequently, above all in the gorges.

The flowers of Ebenus cretica *(above)*
and Petromarula pinnata *(below) enliven*
the rupestrian environments.

PETROMARULA PINNATA (L.) A. DC. 108
(Campanulaceae)

The springtime traveler to Crete is inevitably struck by this beautiful plant with its inflorescences up to one meter in length. The numerous flowers, in various shades of pale blue or violet, have narrow petals and red anthers. The basal leaves are deeply lobed. The plant is endemic to Crete, where it lives on calcareous slopes and old walls.

EBENUS CRETICA L. 109
(Leguminosae)

This highly decorative shrub, with showy flowers and a long spring flowering time, is of Asiatic origin and, among the endemic plants of Crete, is surely the most widespread. It is found on the rocky slopes, in the gorges, in the garrigues, and sometimes along the roadsides. The pink flowers are arranged in terminal inflorescences with silvery-grey hairs. The leaves are likewise silvery and composed of 3 to 5 elliptical segments. The at times quite extensive colonies formed by *E. creticus* L. are habitats of Community interest.

108

09

110

111

112

INULA CANDIDA (L.) CASS. [110]
(Compositae)

As the name suggests, the leaves, stem, and the involucre of the flowerhead of this member of the family Compositae are covered with a dense white down. The leaves are ovate-lanceolate with entire margins and prominent venation. The flowers (May-June) are yellow and borne in flowerheads.

CAMPANULA PELVIFORMIS LAM. [111]
(Campanulaceae)

This Bellflower, endemic to Crete, grows in the eastern portion of the island on calcareous slopes, in the woods, and on roadside embankments. The stalked basal leaves are ovate and hairy with crenate margins. The stem is also hairy and bears sessile leaves. The flowers, which appear in April and May, are up to 3 cm in length, violet-blue, broad by bell-shaped, and slightly swollen at about half their length. The sepals are three times the length of the ovary; the stigma is divided into three parts.

CAMPANULA TUBULOSA LAM. [112]
(Campanulaceae)

Another Bellflower endemic to Crete, but one that differently from the previous example lives in the west-central part of the island. The stem is pubescent, with stalked, ovate-oblong leaves. The violet corolla has a long tube, as the species name suggests, and the lobes of the calyx are twice as long as the ovary. Grows in damp rock crevices in shady positions.

AETHIONEMA SAXATILE (L.) R. BR. IN W. T. AITON SUBSP. CRETICUM (BOISS. & HELDR.) [113]
(Cruciferae)

The Burnt Candytuft is a small plant, growing to a maximum height of 30 cm, with erect or prostrate stems and ovate-oblong leaves. The white, pink, or purple flowers are borne in small, almost spherical inflorescences. The fruit is a small obovate or orbicular silicula. Although *A. saxatile* is quite widespread throughout the island, it is easiest to find in the high mountains, where it grows in crevices in the rock.

114

ONOSMA ERECTUM SM. SUBSP. ERECTUM [114]
(Boraginaceae)

A plant growing to 25 cm, with narrowly lanceolate leaves covered with stellate hairs. The flowers (April-May) have yellow petals up to 24 mm in length, fused. Grows on the cliffs but may also be found in other rupestrian environments, in the cypress woods of western Crete, and in any case up to 1800 meters above sea level.

LINUM ARBOREUM L. [115]
(Linaceae)

A plant with woody stems rising from a basal rosette of thick, persistent, spatulate leaves with a thickened horny margin. The yellow flowers, 2 to 3 cm in diameter, appear between March and May. *L. arboreum* L. grows on cliffs and on rocky terrain and prefers calcareous substrates.

SCORZONERA CRETICA WILLD. [116]
(Compositae)

The hairy, linear leaves of the Cretan Viper's-Grass are up to 30 cm long, and are longest and most evident near the base of the plant. The yellow flowers (March-May) are arranged in flowerheads as large as 5 cm diameter. Although it is easily identifiable thanks to its fruit, the hairy achene typical of the genus Scorzonera, surmounted by a

115

116

long feathery pappus, S. cretica Willd. is highly variable as to hairiness and leaf size. It lives on the cliffs (for example, there are beautiful individuals on the rock walls of the Kourtaliotis Gorge), in the phrygana, and even near the sea, on sandy soil.

SCUTELLARIA SIEBERI BENTH. IN DC. 117
(Labiatae)

The genus name derives from a shield-shaped dorsal protuberance on the calyx. This tomentous plant grows to 60 cm with many basal ramifications; the leaves are ovate, crenate and up to 4 and occasionally 5 cm in length. The terminal spike inflorescences bear flowers with whitish corollas with rosy veinings on the upper lip (April-June). Endemic to Crete, *S. sieberi* Benth. grows from sea level to 950 meters altitude on calcareous cliffs and detritus. It can be observed with relative ease in the Valley of the Dead, on the rock faces of the gorge near Káto Zákros.

*

At the base of the rock walls there may form detrital accumulations of rocky elements of small and medium size that create an incoherent stratum. Only a few plants can live in such an environment: among these are *Ricotia cretica*, a Crucifer with slender stalks and violet flowers, and *Scutellaria hirta*, with its velvety leaves. Both are endemic to Crete. On the mountains, above 1400 meters altitude, it is instead possible to observe more or less extensive colonies of the cushion-like *Aubrieta deltoidea*, a plant that outside of this habitat is widely cultivated as a decorative element for rock gardens. Along the road from Gourniá to Tourloti the visitor to Crete will encounter an example of a broad accumulation of detritus with typical plants. The plant communities on gravel and detritus are habitats of Community interest.

CENTAUREA RAPHANINA SM. SUBSP. RAPHANINA 123
(Compositae)

The basal rosette is made up of entire or more frequently lyrate-pinnate, scarious leaves with pubescent surfaces. The pink flowers are arranged in almost spherical flowerheads that are sessile or on short stalks. The involucre of the flowerhead tapers at the base and may reach 2 cm diameter; the bracts bear a terminal spine 2 to 9 mm in length. The subspecies *raphanina* is endemic to Crete and lives in crevices in the rocks and in the phrygana, from sea level to 2300 meters; it may also be found growing on old walls.

RUTA CHALEPENSIS L. SUBSP. CHALEPENSIS & RUTA CHALEPENSIS L. SUBSP. FUMARIIFOLIA (BOISS. & HELDR.) NYMAN 124
(Rutaceae)

The first-named plant is a subshrub to 50 to 70 cm height, set apart by its strong odor and the translucid glands on the leaves, which are 2 to 10 cm in length and pinnate. It contains a volatile oil (*oleum rutae*) that would seem to have been used in ancient times as a condiment as well as a cure for hysteria, vertigo, amenorrhoea, and rheumatic pains. The flowers (April-May) are small,

123

124

125

with 4 or 5 fringed yellow petals, one cm in length. This species lives in rocky environments and its easy to individuate along the beds of the gorges. *Ruta chalepensis* L. subsp. *fumariifolia* is similar to subsp. *chalepensis* but is smaller in size and its leaves are divided into linear segments.

PHLOMIS LANATA WILLD. 125
(Labiatae)

This Phlomis, endemic to Crete, grows to 50 cm. The leathery basal leaves, covered with stellate hairs on both surfaces, are oblong or broadly elliptical and 1.5 to 2.8 cm long, with crenulate margins; the leafstalk is one cm long. The leaves of the flower stalks are sub-sessile and suborbiculate. The

flowers, with a yellow corolla 20 to 23 mm long, are grouped in verticillasters composed of from 2 to 10 flowers; the bracteoles have stellate hairs. Differently from *Phlomis fruticosa*, this species is found mainly in the east-central region of Crete, where it grows in the beds of the gorges, in the phrygana, in clearings in the cypress woods, and on the cliffs. It is not always easy to distinguish among the various species of *Phlomis* since they often hybridize.

OSYRIS ALBA L. 126
(Santalaceae)

Although of the Sandalwood family, one common name of this plant is 'broom' due to the

126

127

resemblance of its erect, angular branches to those of the true Brooms. It is a semi-parasite of trees and shrubs, with small, single-veined lanceolate leaves that can be seen on the plant in winter since they are almost totally caducous in summer. *O. alba* L. is dioecious, with yellow flowers that are sweetly scented but tiny. The fruits, small red drupes, were used in times past to produce a detergent substance for cosmetic applications. The plant thrives in rocky areas and along the beds of the torrents that run through the gorges.

CICHORIUM SPINOSUM L.
(Compositae)

A perennial herb to 20 cm, densely and intricately branched from the base upward, with spiny upper branches. The leaves are fleshy and elliptical in form; those at the base of the plant and deeply cut or lobed. The light blue flowerheads are subtended by oval bracts and may be either apical or axillary and solitary or in clusters of 2 to 4. This plant flowers from June through October and grows on rocky terrains, in crevices in the coastal rock, and in the phrygana.

ARISTOLOCHIA CRETICA LAM. 128
(Aristolochiaceae)

This plant, endemic to Crete, grows mostly in the eastern part of the island, where it can be found on rocky calcareous soils as well

128

129

130

as in the phrygana, in wooded areas, and at the bases of dry walls. It is a climber with stems up to 60 cm tall that bear rounded leaves, 5 cm in width, with undulate margins and a cordate base. The distinctive flowers are irregular, in the form of a long, strongly curved, U-shaped tube, the interior of which is covered with long white hairs; they are brown with a greenish base.

MUSCARI SPREITZENHOFERI (HELDR. EX OSTERM.) VIERH. 129
(Liliaceae)

The scape of this Grape Hyacinth may be as tall as 5 to 15 cm. At the base are 3 to 5 linear leaves, up to 20 cm in length and 8 to 12 mm in width, the outer leaves being widest. The flowers are grouped in a lax raceme: the fertile flowers (greater in number) are small, dark brown, and urn-shaped, with a lighter base supported by a patent peduncle, and are found in the lower portion of the inflorescence; the sterile flowers are instead pale blue with brown veins and form a cluster at the apex of the raceme. This plant is endemic to Crete, where it occupies rocky habitats from the crevices in the rock to the bare soil of the phrygana, although it may also be found in the sandy coastal areas.

LEGOUSIA SPECULUM-VENERIS (L.) CHAIX 130
(Campanulaceae)

This hairy annual herb has an erect, branched stem and alternate leaves that are somewhat pruinous. The flowers, which appear in May, are violet or purple, sometimes with blue overtones, and open widely to form a blunt five-pointed star. The fruit is a capsule 10 to 15 cm in length. The Large Venus's Looking-Glass, as this plant is commonly called, grows on rocky soils and on detritus.

ORIGANUM ONITES L. 131
(Labiatae)

An erect, aromatic dwarf shrub to 60 cm, covered with a light down. The oval or rounded leaves are slightly toothed and sometimes cordate at the base; the upper leaves are sessile. The white flowers, 4 to 5 mm long, are arranged in dense cylindrical inflorescences; the calyx has a single lip. The leaves of the Pot Marjoram are dried and used as seasoning.

131

WETLANDS

There are two lakes on Crete, both located near Haniá: the natural Lake Kournas and the man-made Lake Agía. The perennial watercourses are few, while the streams that dry up in summer are more numerous; there are also a few coastal marshes, generally near the mouths of the rivers. Along the torrential watercourses and on gravelly substrates we find Oleander and Chaste Tree formations and gallery woods of Plane trees. At the edges of the lakes and the marshes there live herbaceous plants such as *Lythrum junceum*, with its violet flowers, and *Oenanthe pimpinelloides*, an umbellifer with white flowers.

Right, a Plane woods; bottom, Lythrum junceum in flower on the banks of the man-made Lake Agía.

75

PLATANUS ORIENTALIS L. 132 133
(Platanaceae)

132

The common Plane tree, which may grow as tall as 30 meters, has a distinctive dark brown bark that peels away in long patches with age, palmate-lobate leaves with 5 to 7 cuts, and flowers arranged in dense, spherical, pendent inflorescences. This tree lives in the wet areas along the torrents that run through the gorges. It forms gallery woods or small groves from sea level to 1200 meters altitude, and is often associated with Oleander and the Chaste Tree, with *Cyclamen creticum* and *Dracunculus vulgaris* in the underwood; these very beautiful woodlands are included among the habitats of Community interest. *P. orientalis* L. is also frequently planted in the villages because of the pleasant shade afforded by its crown in summer. Mythology recounts that Zeus, after having abducted Europa, married her in the shade of a Planetree, identified with the monumental individual located near the Roman theater at Gortyn in the Plain of Messará, that thenceforth ceased to drop its leaves in winter.

133

NERIUM OLEANDER L. 134
(Apocynaceae)

The Oleander is an extremely poisonous plant that if accidentally swallowed can cause serious illness and even death. It is nevertheless much appreciated for its ornamental value, with its pink flowers 3 to 5 cm in diameter that persist through the summer; it is also easy to cultivate due to its resistance to drought, its capacity to support drastic pruning, and its generally limited requirements. For these reasons it is widely grown in gardens and many cultivars have been created. The evergreen leaves are linear-lanceolate with a pronounced center venation, and arranged in verticils of three. The fruit is a large follicle that at maturity releases a great number of seeds topped by a shock of hairs. The Oleander is often found along rivers and smaller watercourses; it associates with the Chaste Tree to form extensive, highly decorative colonies that are included among the habitats worthy of Community conservation efforts.

134

Vitex agnus-castus L. [135]
(Verbenaceae)

The genus name derives from the
Latin *viere* (to plait): in fact, the
strong, flexible branches of the
Chaste Tree were used to bind
slaves. A legend also tells how
Ulysses used these branches to
bind his companions under the
bodies of the sheep to escape from
Polyphemus' cave. The species
name, instead, evokes chastity:
hagnos (Greek) and *castus* (Latin)
both mean 'chaste'. Hera, the
protectress of marriage, was born
under this shrub; women who
would declare their chastity during
the celebrations in honor of
Demeter lay on a pallet plaited of
its branches. In the centuries that
followed, the plant, considered an
anaphrodisiac, was planted near
the convents; it has also been
demonstrated that the flowered
tips of the stems and the fruits
have sedative properties. This plant
is also known by the name of
Monk's Pepper, due to the spicy
odor of the branches and fruits.
It grows, together with the
Oleander, along the seasonal
watercourses and is frequently
found along the beds of the
gorges; it is very decorative thanks
to its compound palmate leaves
and above all to its flowers, which
vary from white through violet and
are arranged in very showy axillary
cymes.

135

Lythrum junceum Banks & Sol. in Russell [136]
(Lythraceae)

A perennial herb with numerous
quadrangular stems, up to 70 cm
in height and suffused with red
especially nearer the base.
The oblong-linear leaves are
opposite below and alternate on
the upper part of the stem.
The flowers (March-May) are
purple with a lighter spot at the
base. On Crete, this plant is quite
common along the rivers and in
the wetlands.

Oenanthe pimpinelloides L. [137]
(Umbelliferae)

A perennial herb with a channeled
stem 3 mm in diameter and up to

one meter tall. The roots have
egg-shaped tubers. The basal
leaves are two-pinnate, while the
cauline leaves are pinnate with
entire linear lobes. The white

flowers (March-May) are grouped
in terminal umbels with 6 to 15
rays. The Corky-Fruited Water
Dropwort grows in west-central
Crete.

136

137

GORGES

The gorges are probably the most distinctive of Crete's natural habitats, and certainly the most interesting from the botanical point of view. They were formed about 14 million years ago, when movements of the Earth's crust produced cleavages: later, the action of rainwater contributed to deepening the rifts in the rock.

On Crete, the gorges are numerous and almost all have a north-south orientation. The best known is that of Samaria, in the Haniá Prefecture: it is one of the deepest in Europe and is now part of a National Park founded in 1962. It is open to visitors for a total of about 18 kilometers, from 1200 meters above sea level at Xilóskalo on the Omalós highland, down to the Libyan Sea on the southern coast of the island. The gorge is home to many animals, among which the wild goat of Crete (somewhat resembling a steinbok), the badger, the Cretan weasel, the salamanders, the eagle, and the vulture.

Other famous and spectacular gorges that may be traveled at least in part are the Imbros Gorge, again in the prefecture of Haniá, Kourtaliotis (Rethymnon), and the Valley of the Dead, at the extreme eastern tip of the island near Káto Zákros (Lassíthi).

The gorges are composite environments embracing many very different habitats: shaded or sunny rupestrian surfaces, steep slopes, watercourses, phrygana or garrigue formations, and woods alternate to form even very complex mosaics. Together with the calcareous cliffs and the mountain peaks of the rest of the island, these formations are among the environments richest in endemic

Rupestrian habitats and wet areas characterize the gorges. Top, the entrance to the Samaria Gorge; above and right, the Kourtaliotis Gorge.

species, above all chasmophytes, which have been able to differentiate and escape the action of man and of animals thanks to the isolation and the inaccessibility of the places they have colonized.

The cliff formations predominate in the gorges, and therefore many of the plants that grow here are chasmophytes, including certain of those already described in the sections on other habitats. It is in fact possible to find *Ebenus cretica, Petromarula pinnata, Scorzonera cretica, Campanula tubulosa, C. pelviformis, Scutellaria sieberi*, and two yellow-flowered plants, *Linum arboreum* and *Onosma erectum*. Where the slope of the rock is gentler and an adequate soil layer has formed, we can observe representatives typical of the garrigue, the phrygana, and the maquis formations, including *Anthyllis hermanniae, Euphorbia acanthothamnos, Ballota acetabulosa*, the Lentisc, and various species of *Cistus* and *Phlomis*. Most of the watercourses that run through the gorges are dry in summer: along their beds we will find beautiful exemplars of *Platanus orientalis* (which may form small woods), and the Oleander and *Vitex agnus-castus*, with their prolonged flowering periods. *Osyris alba, Phlomis lanata*, and *Ruta chalepensis* grow in the beds of the gorges.

Exploring these valleys is always a rewarding experience, since they host many plants that we are used to seeing in different environments. The Samaria Gorge, in particular, displays an astounding change in the vegetation from the point of departure in the mountains toward the foot on the Libyan Sea: at the beginning of the descent we can observe especially beautiful and majestic ex-

The gorge called the Valley of the Dead, in eastern Crete, can be traveled its entire length.

The most famous of Crete's gorges are Samaria (top left), the Valley of the Dead (above) and Kourtaliotis (left).

amples of pine and cypress, small cushions of *Aubrieta deltoidea* and *Aethionema saxatile,* and the showy flowers of *Linum arboreum.* Further on, we see the phrygana vegetation, the cliffs with *Ebenus* and *Petromarula*, the mountain streams, the Plane woods and the stands of Oleanders and Chaste Trees. At the seaside, finally, in Agía Rouméli, is one of Crete's few pebbly beaches, formed of an accumulation of rounded stones among which we find only a few specialized plants that form very open communities composed, for example, of *Cakile maritima, Matthiola tricuspidata,* and *Crithmum maritimum,* with no dominant species.

Many of the biocenoses found in the Samaria Gorge, among which the cliffs, the mountain streams, the Oleander and Chaste Tree formations, the Plane woods, and the pebbly beach, are of Community interest.

ANTHROPIZED ENVIRONMENTS

Man has been a long time in Crete: the first colonists are believed to have arrived six to five thousand years before Christ, and so many plants have had time to adapt to the prepotent presence of the newcomer. Most of these are herbs, above all annuals; that is, plants with a short life cycle that have succeeded in adapting to the frequent changes imposed by man on the environment. The plants linked to anthropized environments, called ruderal species, can be found along the roadsides, in the archaeological sites, in waste land, and in cultivated fields. On the old walls, on the ruins of castles, and in the archaeological sites we can find plants that are normally typical of the cliff habitats, such as *Petromarula pinnata*, or the rocky soils, such as *Centaurea* subsp. *raphanina*, *Matthiola tricuspidata*, *Malcolmia*

Top, Field Gladioli in flower along a roadside; bottom, showy blossoms in an olive grove.

Yellow Horned-Poppies in flower.

flexuosa, and *Bryonia cretica.* The roadsides are often enlivened by spreading blotches of color afforded by various species of *Echium,* by *Chrysanthemum coronarium,* by *Gladiolus italicus,* and by two quite showy plants with very beautiful yellow flowers, *Ferula communis* and *Glaucium flavum;* then there are the spiny Compositae like *Galactites tomentosa, Notobasis syriaca, Silybum marianum,* and the *Echinops spinosissimus.* It is also possible to observe white, pink, or more rarely red individuals of the species *Ranunculus asiaticus* and the pink flowers of *Convolvulus althaeoides.* It is only natural that many of the plants listed in this section on anthropized environments also live in such natural environments as the garrigue, the rocky areas, and the coasts.

ECHIUM ITALICUM **L.** SUBSP. *BIEBERSTEINII* (**LACAITA**) **GREUTER & BURDET** 138
(Boraginaceae)

A robust plant growing erect to one meter; hirsute due to the presence of bristles and prickly hairs. During the first year of growth it forms large rosettes of more or less sessile, lanceolate to narrowly elliptical leaves. The many pink or yellowish flowers, with long stamens, are arranged in symmetrical, pyramid-shaped inflorescences. Flowers from April through July on rocky soils, in abandoned fields, and along roadsides.

ECHIUM PLANTAGINEUM **L.** 139
(Boraginaceae)

An annual herb covered with blackish, hispid, glandular hairs. The unlobed leaves are lanceolate or ovate; the basal leaves are larger than the cauline leaves. The violet-blue flowers (April-May), up to 3.5 cm long, are grouped in elongated branched inflorescences. This species is quite common in the agricultural areas of all of southern Europe, where it may form even quite extensive colonies. Flowers from February through July. The roots produce a red dyestuff.

138

ECHIUM ANGUSTIFOLIUM MILL, SUBSP. *ANGUSTIFOLIUM* [140]
(Boraginaceae)

This perennial herb, growing as tall as 80 cm, is usually branched from the base upward and very hairy over its entire surface. The hairs are variously distributed and are of two types: some areas are densely short-hairy and other areas are characterized by sparse long bristles with knob-like bases. The leaves are linear. The flowers are 15 to 25 mm in length, and red tending to violet or to whitish. This subspecies is found in anthropized areas, often near the sea.

CHRYSANTHEMUM CORONARIUM L. [141]
(Compositae)

The Crown Daisy is an herb with numerous erect, branched stems bearing sessile or semi-amplexicaul two-pinnately-lobed leaves. The flowers appear from March through May in flowerheads up to 6 cm in diameter. This species counts two varieties, both of which are found on Crete: *Chrysanthemum coronarium* L. var. *coronarium*, with entirely yellow, ligulate flowers, and *Chrysanthemum coronarium* L. var. *discolor* d'Urv., with ligulate flowers that are yellow in the basal portion and white in the distal part. Grows in open areas, along the roads, and on the sandy coasts; it sometimes forms dense and extensive populations that appear as bright blotches of color. The young shoots were eaten as recently as the last century; in more remote times, it was believed that this plant could protect against sorcery, and it is perhaps for this reason that it was used in the decoration of the sanctuaries.

GLAUCIUM FLAVUM CRANTZ [142]
(Papaveraceae)

The Yellow Horned-Poppy is widely distributed in the sandy and rocky coastal habitats, but may also be found growing along the roadsides. Its branched stems, up to one meter in length, bear numerous showy flowers, up to 9 cm in diameter, of a beautiful bright yellowcolor.

140

141

After the flowering period, which lasts from March through May, the fruits appear: these are very long, slender capsules up to 30 cm in length. The bases of the pinnate leaves, which are light green or blue-green, clasp the stem; the lower leaves are longer than those higher up the plant. This plant was used in antiquity as a purgative.

GALACTITES TOMENTOSA MOENCH [143]
(Compositae)

This plant is characterized, as the species name suggests, by the white wooly felt that covers the stem and the lower surfaces of the leaves. It is annual or biennial with an erect caulis up to 50 cm tall that may be simple or branched above. The leaves are narrow and lanceolate with triangular segments that terminate in a slender, prickly yellow spine; the upper leaf surface is glabrous green while the underside is densely white-downy. The pinkish-purple, branched flowerheads are not very large and appear in involucres of green scaley bracts from February through May.

142

143

GLADIOLUS ITALICUS **MILL.** [145]
(Iridaceae)

The Field Gladiolus is one of the numerous plants that the ancient Greeks called *Hyakinthos* and that were linked to the legend that recounts how from the blood of Hyacinthus, accidentally slain by the god Apollo, there sprang a flower with a letter-shaped (A or V) mark on the lower lip interpreted as reading *"aiai, alas, alas"*.
The common gladiolus is a perennial herb to 80 cm, with a green stem and long, linear leaves. The unilateral lax spikes are formed of up to 10 flowers each; the flowers are bright pink, lighter inside with dark spots. The plant is widely distributed on Crete and sometimes forms extensive, very beautiful colonies.

FERULA COMMUNIS **L.** SUBSP. *COMMUNIS* [144]
(Umbelliferae)

An eye-catching herbaceous perennial that may reach even 3 meters in height during the flowering season. The inflorescences are branched umbels composed of bright yellow flowers; the leaves are divided repeatedly into linear segments. The pith of the Giant Fennel burns slowly in the hardened stem, and can be carried alight: legend has it that this was the means used by Prometheus to convey to mankind the gift of heavenly fire stolen from Vulcan's hearth despite Zeus' prohibition.

145

144

NOTOBASIS SYRIACA (L.) CASS. IN CUZIER [146]
(Compositae)

An annual herb from 30 to 150 cm, glabrous or with whitish hairs and an erect, striated stem. The large leaves are usually glabrous on the upper surface and spiderwebby underneath, with more or less deeply-lobed margins and teeth that terminate in spines; the cauline leaves are spinose, linear, and deeply cut into linear segments; they are characteristically violet-hued with silver veinings. The flowers, of an intense purple color, are grouped in flowerheads 3 to 5 cm in diameter (April-June). The uppermost leaves extend beyond the flowerheads.

SILYBUM MARIANUM (L.) GAERTN. [147]
(Compositae)

A large, spiny annual or sometimes biennial herb that may grow as tall as 2.5 meters. The striate stem is simple or more commonly branched. The leaves are typically green with white variegations and are generally large in size. The pinkish flowers are borne in flowerheads 6 to 10 cm in width, and appear in April and May. According to legend, the white spots on the leaves derive from the drops of milk scattered by the Virgin as she fled to subtract Jesus from persecution by Herod. The edible parts of the Milk Thistle are the stems, if harvested before flowering, the young leaves, the roots, and the flowerheads.

ECHINOPS SPINOSISSIMUS TURRA [148]
(Compositae)

This representative of the Globe Thistles grows as tall as 1.5 meters and, as its species name implies, bears strong spines. The erect stem is covered with a spiderwebby glandular down. The leaves are two-pinnate, with a dense white down on the underside.
This species differs from the other Compositae for having flowerheads composed of single flowers (May-June); together, the flowerheads form a pale blue spherical inflorescence incorporating spiny bracts.

146

147

148

149

150

151

152

ANCHUSA HYBRIDA TEN. 149
(Boraginaceae)

This annual or biennial herb, growing to from 20 to 50 cm, is densely pubescent and often has long rigid bristles and erect stems that are branched from the base upward. The leaves are lanceolate with undulate margins; the basal leaves are appressed to the ground. The elongated lax inflorescences bear purple or violet flowers and are subtended by ovate scales that vary in color from white through pink. Flowers in April in the vineyards and in other anthropized areas.

CYNOGLOSSUM CRETICUM MILL. 150
(Boraginaceae)

The Blue Hound's Tongue is an erect plant to 30 cm with oblong, lanceolate, densely hairy leaves. The flowers, borne on short branched cymes, are purple in the bud but open bluer with inky-dark veinings. Flowering time is from March through June. This plant is common in the abandoned fields and olive-groves of the southeastern Mediterranean regions.

TRAGOPOGON SINUATUS AVÉ-LALL 151
(Compositae)

This plant, up to 50 cm in height and occasionally even twice that tall, was called Goat's-Beard by Theophrastus, perhaps due to the look of the flowerhead at the moment of fructification. The flowers, which appear in March and April, are pink or purple and grouped in large flowerheads each subtended by 8 elongated bracts. The leaves are linear with pointed tips. The cylindrical rootstock, White Salsify, is edible and sweet flavored; it is sometimes cultivated.

STACHYS CRETICA L. SUBSP. *CRETICA* 152
(Labiatae)

A densely white-felted perennial herb with an erect stem. The oblong or oval leaves are rounded at the base and greyish in color; the surface is visibile between the hairs. The pink or purple flowers are arranged in verticils that are generally rather distant. Flowers in April and May on rocky terrains, along roadsides, and also in the sandy coastal habitats.

153

DRACUNCULUS VULGARIS SCHOTT 155
(Araceae)

A highly singular plant up to one meter, with white-veined, lobed leaves on long stalks. The leaves envelop the inflorescence with basal bracts mottled like snakeskin. The small unisexual flowers are arranged along an axis called a spadix, which is enclosed for almost its entire length by the spathe, a wide membranous sheet with slightly wavy margins; both organs are purple in color. The plant emits an unpleasant odor at flowering time (April-May). The fruits are red berries. The showy flowers of this plant have always attracted attention and clearly provided the inspiration for the ornamental motifs in the Minoan pictorial decoration of a number of sarcophagi found on Crete.

LUPINUS ALBUS L. SUBSP. *ALBUS* 153
(Leguminosae)

This plant was cultivated in Egypt from 2000 BC onward; it spread among the Greeks and later the Romans, who ate the cooked seeds on feast days. The seeds of the White Lupin are still eaten cooked: they are rich in mineral salts and if toasted provide a surrogate for coffee. The plant, up to one meter in height, is hairy, with compound leaves.
The flowers are white, sometimes streaked blue at the apex, and grouped in racemes. The long legumes contain light-colored seeds. On Crete there are three other species of Lupin, with flowers of varying shades of blue (*L. angustifolius* L., *L. micranthus* Guss., and *L. pilosus* L.).

ANEMONE CORONARIA L. 154
(Ranunculaceae)

The Crown Anemone is a pretty perennial, growing to about 30 cm. The long-stalked basal leaves are divided into 3 parts; the other leaves are similar but with a shorter petiole. The showy flowers, which often have a white spot at the base of the petals, may be of various colors (pink, red, blue, sky blue, violet) and may be as large as 8 cm in diameter. The Crown Anemone flowers between January and April. It grows in cultivated and abandoned fields, but it is also commonly planted in gardens; there are various cultivars with single and double flowers. Dioscurides prescribed the juice of the anemone root, to be taken as nose-drops, as a cure for severe headaches.

154

156

RHAGADIOLUS STELLATUS (**L.**) GAERTN. 156
(Compositae)

An annual with erect or prostrate stems covered with coarse hairs. The oblong leaves are broadest at the middle and provided with small teeth; the leaves nearer the top of the plant are sometimes oval or lanceolate. The long-stalked yellow flowerheads bear only a few flowers in lax spreading panicles surrounded by 5 to 8 slender, linear bracts. Flowers between March and June. The long, pointed achenes are enclosed by enlarged bracts, with slightly curved tips, to form a large, 7- to 8-pointed star.

157

CONVOLVULUS ALTHAEOIDES **L.** 157
(Convolvulacee)

This hairy perennial, which goes by the common English name of Mallow-Leaved Bindweed, has long and flexuous climbing or creeping stems that branch out considerably along the ground. The lower leaves are rounded, while those higher up the stems are deeply lobed. From March to June the stems are covered with showy pink flowers, more intensely-hued at the center with funnel-shaped corollas 3 to 4 cm in diameter that close in the evening. This plant is often found on walls, rocky soils, in waste land and in fields near the coasts.

*

The term 'nitrophilous ruderal species' is used to describe plants linked to the presence of grazing animals: *Ecballium elaterium*, various species of *Urtica*, *Byronia cretica*, and all those plants that thrive on substrates rich in organic wastes.

ECBALLIUM ELATERIUM **L. A. RICH.** IN BORY 158
(Cucurbitaceae)

The Squirting Cucumber has creeping stems and rough-surfaced triangular leaves; the yellow flowers, borne at the axils of the leaves, attract a great number of pollinating bees. This plant is

158

159

peculiar, and quite amusing, because if the ripe fruit is pressed (or sometimes even simply touched), it literally squirts its small seeds (in a pulpy liquid) to great distances. The plant is poisonous, even though in ancient times it was widely used in herbal medicine.

URTICA PILULIFERA L. [159]
(Urticaceae)

An annual herb as tall as one meter, with leaves 2 to 6 cm in length borne on long petioles. The male and female flowers are borne separately, in elongated and rounded inflorescences, respectively. Flowers in March and April. While not very common, it may be found near buildings and enclosures for animals.

BRYONIA CRETICA L.
SUBSP. *CRETICA* [160]
(Cucurbitaceae)

A dioecious climber with hispid stems up to 4 meters in length. The palmate-lobate leaves are silky, with white spots in along the veins. The male and female flowers are small and whitish, with a funnel-shaped corolla; the fruits are red berries with small white blotches that appear before ripening. All parts of this plant are poisonous.

160

GLOSSARY

Achene. An indehiscent dry fruit containing a single seed.

Acorn. A dry indehiscent fruit (achene) that is oval in form and seated in or surrounded at the base by a hemispherical involucre called a cupule. Typical of the oaks (Fagaceae).

Annual. A plant that completes its life-cycle (germination from seed, flowering, fruiting, death) in a single season.

Anther. The terminal portion of the stamen in which the pollen is produced.

Anthropization. The actions of man that aim at transformation and alteration of the territory to adapt it to serve his interests and needs.

Appressed. Pressed close to another organ (e.g. hairs close to a stem).

Association. A fundamental unit in ecological community organization having two or more life forms sharing a similar environment.

Axil. The angle between the leaf and the stem.

Axis. Flower- or leaf-bearing stem (primary axis) or branch or peduncle (secondary axis).

Berry. An indehiscent fruit with one or more seeds in a fleshy pulp; the integuments of the seeds are lignified.

Biennial. A plant that completes its life-cycle over the course of two seasons, germinating in the first year and flowering, fruiting and dying in the second.

Biocenosis. An assemblage of different organisms inhabiting a region uniform in environmental conditions. From the Greek *bios* (life) and *koinosis* (sharing, common).

Blade. The broad portion of a leaf.

Bract. A modified and usually small leaf (often scale-like, sometimes leaf-like) located near a flower or an inflorescence.

Bracteole. A bract on a secondary branch of an inflorescence.

Bud. An undeveloped shoot made up of rudimentary foliage or floral leaves.

Bulb. The ovoid underground part of certain plants (mostly monocotyledonous herbs) composed of a mass of overlapping fleshy or membranous leaves on a short stem base.

Bulbous. Of a plant growing from a bulb.

Caducous. Falling off easily or before the usual time.

Calyx. The outer whorl of a flower, composed of the sepals which envelop the flower and protect it in the bud.

Capsule. A dry or leathery dehiscent fruit composed of one or more carpels with one or more cavities containing seeds.

Carina. Or keel: the unit formed by the two lower petals of the papilionaceous flowers of the Leguminosae and the Polygalaceae.

Carpel. One of the compartments or units making up the ovary of a seed plant, comprising the innermost whorl of a flower.

Cauline. Belonging to or growing on a stem; specifically, growing on the upper portion of a stem.

Caulis. Stem or stalk.

Chasmophyte. A plant adapted to growing in the crevices of rocks.

Chlorophyll. Pigment that captures light energy: from the Greek *chloro* (green) and *phyllon* (leaf). See **photosynthesis**.

CITES. Convention on International Trade in Endangered Species of Wild Fauna and Flora, ratified on 1 July 1975 and now signed by more than 100 countries worldwide.

Clade. A flattened modified stem with 1 or 2 internodes that has the form and function of a leaf.

Compound. An organ, generally a leaf, formed of several elements.

Cone. See **strobilus**.

Cordate. Heart-shaped.

Corolla. Collective name for the petals that form the involucre of a flower.

Crenate. With rounded indentations or notches.

Crenulate. Minutely indented.

Crucifer. A plant of the family Cruciferae; a cress.

Culm. A hollow or pithy herbaceous stem, typical of the family Graminaceae.

Cultivar. A cultivated variety obtained from a spontaneous plant through complex processes of selection and hybridization. The term was introduced to botanical language in 1952, when during the 13th Horticultural Congress it was decided to apply it to cultivated varieties of plants to distinguish them from natural varieties. The latter term is now reserved for use with reference to spontaneous plants.

Cupule. An cup-shaped involucre of more or less appressed scales of varying length that surrounds in part the fruit of the plants of the family Fagaceae.

Cushion. Hemispherical plant form.

Cyathia. A type of inflorescence peculiar to the Spurges (*Euphorbiaceae*) consisting of a cup-like involucre surrounding several male flowers (often reduced to the stamen alone) and one female flower (reduced to the pistil). In the dioecious species, which are quite frequent in the genus *Euphorbia*, each involucre contains only the male flowers or a single female flower.

Cyme. An inflorescence terminating in an apical flower.

Decussate. Of opposite leaves arranged in pairs, each pair at right angles to the next pair above or below.

Deciduous. Having non-persistent leaves, flowers, etc., which fall at the end of the their functional period. Having or made up of deciduous parts (as a deciduous tree).

Dehiscent. Splitting open to release the seeds.

Dioecious. Of a species having the (male) staminate flowers in one individual and the (female) pistillate flowers in another.

Drupe. An indehiscent fruit with fleshy outer strata enveloping the lignified inner stratum (stone). which contains the seed or seeds.

Ecology. The science of the interrelationships among living organisms and the environment in which they live. The term was coined in 1869 by the German biologist E. Haeckel.

Ecosystem. The set of living organisms and non-biological constituents (substrate, climate, solar radiation, etc.) that interact in a given area.

Elliptical. Thinner at the base and the apex with the broadest portion near the center.

Endemic. Exclusive to a given area; may refer to species, genus or even family.

Epichilium. See **labellum**.

Family. In zoological and botanical classification, a group of related plants or animals forming a category ranking above a genus and below an order.

Flora. The plants characteristic of, peculiar to, or adapted to living in a particular situation (geographical area, country, etc.).

Floret. One of the individual flowers making up a flowerhead.

Flowerhead. An inflorescence, typical of the family Compositae, consisting of a tight, formal head of ligulate and tubulous flowers on a flattened axis of an called a receptacle or torus.

Follicle. A dry, dehiscent monocarpellary fruit opening along only one suture

Formation. A unit of study of vegetation, comprising the aggregate of the forms of the individuals that share similar ecological conditions.

Galbulus. A spherical cone, as of that of the Cupressaceae; may be dry with wide woody scales (cypress) or fleshy and compact (juniper).

Garrigue. A vegetation formation typical of the western and eastern Mediterranean, with sclerophyllous shrubs and subshrubs, generally graze- and fire-resistant.

Genus. A taxonomic category ranking between the family and the species, comprising a group of structurally or phylogenetically related species or an isolated species exhibiting unusual differentiation.

Geophyte. A plant with an underground organ, generally a bulb or a tuber.

Glabrous. Having a smooth even surface devoid of hairs or down.

Gland. An organ secreting salt, water, sugar solutions, or other substances.

Glandular. Containing, bearing or made up of glands, often seen as dots.

Glaucous. Having a powdery or waxy coating that gives a frosted appearance.

Glomerule. A globular inflorescence resembling the flowerhead of a member of the family Compositae, composed of numerous flowers clustered together.

Gorge. A ravine, canyon, or defile in rock in which a watercourse flows, generally until summer. The gorges are typical of the Balkan area.

Gynostemium. A structure typical of the orchids, in which one or two stamens are fused to the style.

Habitat. The set of climatic and environmental conditions that permit single animal or plant species to live and develop; the kind of site or region naturally or normally preferred by a biological species.

Habitat of Community Interest. A habitat listed in EEC Directive 92/43 promoting 'the preservation, protection and improvement of the quality of the environment, including the conservation of natural habitats and of wild fauna and flora' at the European Community level.

Herb. Any green-stemmed plant that does not develop a woody stem.

Herbaceous. Of plant organs that are green and with a leaf-like texture.

Hispid. Rough or covered with bristles, stiff hairs or minute spines.

Hypochilium. See **labellum**.

Imbricate. Closely and uniformly overlapping like the shingles of a roof.

Indehiscent. Fruits that do not split open to release their seeds.

Inflorescence. A floral axis with its appendages; a flower cluster or sometimes a solitary flower

Internode. The part of the stem between two successive leaf nodes.

Involucre. Flower-bracts forming a cuff or ruff at the base of a flower cluster or flowerhead.

Involute. Curled or curved inward over the upper surface, generally referred to a leaf margin.

Keel. A biological process forming a ridge like the keel of a boat.

Labellum. Literally, 'small lip'. A complex tepal typical of the orchids, generally the showiest element of the flower. It may be gibbous, may be entire or lobed, variously colored and/or hairy. It is opposed to the stamens and is made up of a proximal (upper) portion called the hypochilium, a median portion called the mesochilium, and a distal (terminal) portion called the epichilium.

Lamina. The blade or expanded part of a foliage leaf.

Lanceolate. Shaped like a lance head, wider at the base and tapering to a point at the apex.

Laurophyllous. Of plant species with broad, thick, persistent leaves with little sclerenchymatous tissue, similar to those of the Laurel (*Laurus nobilis*).

Lax. Loose, as of an inflorescence in which the florets are not densely packed.

Leaflet. One of the divisions of a compound leaf.

Legume. A dehiscent fruit formed of a single carpel, typical of the family Leguminosae, which at maturity opens along the two sides to release the seeds.

Ligulate. Of a flower with a ribbon-shaped corolla. In the Compositae, the external flowers are ligulate and the inner flowers are tubular.

Lithophyte. A plant that has adapted to living on a rocky substrate.

Lobed. Divided, but not separated entirely, into various parts by deeper or shallower notches.

Lyrate. Of a leaf divided into segments, of which the uppermost is clearly larger than the others.

Maquis. A dense and intricate vegetation formation dominated by evergreen shrubs. From the Corsican *maquis*, thicket.

Melliferous. Of a plant supplying abundant pollen or nectar to bees, which transform it to produce honey and related products.

Monocotyledonous. A plant having a single cotyledon (the first leaf developed by a germinating plant; also called seed leaf).

Monospecific. Containing or comprising a single species.

Mucronate. Ending in a mucro (abrupt sharp point or process).

Naturalized species. An exotic species capable of reproducing naturally in areas outside its native distribution area.

Nectary. A glandular organ of the flower or leaf that produces nectar, a sugary liquid.

Needle. A cylindrical, rigid, pointed leaf, like those of the pines.

Nitrophilous. Preferring or thriving in a soil rich in assimilable nitrogen.

Node. The modified point on a stem or similar structure at which subsidiary parts originate.

Nutrients. Organic or inorganic substances required for the correct growth and reproduction of living things.

Obconical. Conical in form with the apex below (upside-down cone).

Oblanceolate. Inversely lanceolate.

Oblong. Longer than wide, with parallel sides for the greater part of the length.

Obovate. Inversely ovate: ovate with the narrower end basal.

Orbiculate. Almost circular.

Ovary. The part of the female reproductive apparatus of seed plants containing the ovules.

Ovate. Egg-shaped, with the basal end broader.

Palmate. Hand-like, with generally shallow lobes, venation, or segments all radiating from a common point.

Panicle. A compound racemose inflorescence composed of an axis with other inflorescences, generally spikes or racemes, which may be sessile or stalked.

Papilla. A small protuberance.

Papilionaceous. Of an irregular flower, typical of the family Leguminosae, formed of 5 petals: the upper standard overlaps the lateral wings, which lie on each side of the lower carina or keel, formed of two fused petals.

Papillate. Covered with or bearing papillae or resembling a papilla.

Pappus. Tufts of bristles, hairs or scales that surmount achenes or fruits; typical of the Compositae.

Parasite. A plant that lives at the expense of another (called the host), obtaining from it its nutriment and causing it damage.

Patent. organ forming a right angle with that on which it is borne.

Peduncle. Generally, the supporting stalk of a leaf, flower, etc.

Pendent. Supported from above; hanging.

Perennate. Living over from season to season; persistent. For example, a rhizome, bulb, or tuber.

Perennial. A plant living for a number of years, and often long-lived.

Perianth. The external sterile parts of a flower (calyx and corolla).

Persistent. Enduring beyond the normal time, as opposed to caducous and deciduous.

Petal. One of the members comprising the corolla of a flower.

Petiole. The leaf-stalk.

Photosynthesis. The process of transformation of the light energy absorbed by the pigments of plant cells containing chlorophyll into chemical energy by which inorganic substances (carbon dioxide, water) are transformed into organic substances (carbohydrates). The

photosynthetic process releases oxygen, a requisite for animal life.

Phrygana. A vegetation formation typical of the eastern Mediterranean, composed of hemispherical, aromatic, spiny shrubs with summer-caducous leaves. The plants are generally graze-resistant and quite distant the ones from the others.

Phytocenosis. The vegetation in a biocenosis.

Phytogeographical area. An area defined on the basis of plant distribution.

Pinnate. Having similar parts arranged on opposite sides of an axis, like a feather; used especially of compound leaves.

Pinnately-lobed. A leaf lobed in a pinnate manner but not separated into leaflets as such.

Pioneer. A plant or animal species capable of colonizing a bare or barren area and initiating a new ecological cycle.

Pistil. The female reproductive organ of a seed plant; the ovary with its appendages the style and the stigma.

Pollination. The act or process of pollinating through transfer of pollen onto the stigma (in the Angiosperms) or the ovule (in the Gymnosperms).

Pollinium. Pollen grains aggregated into a regular mass that can be transported by insects; typical of the orchids.

Population. A group of interbreeding individuals inhabiting a particular area.

Pruinous. Having a waxy coating.

Psammophile. An organism that prefers or thrives in sandy soils or areas.

Pubescent. Covered with fine, soft, short hairs.

Pyriform. Pear-shaped.

Pyrophyte. A plant that is resistant to fire. An active pyrophyte is a plant that spreads or grows better following a fire (for example, plants of the genus *Cistus* with fruits that open when exposed to heat, launching their seeds to great distances, or the Kermes Oak, which radiates many new suckers from the burnt stubs).

Raceme. A type of inflorescence in which the single stalked flowers are borne laterally along a central axis.

Receptacle. The terminal portion of the flower stalk on which are borne part or all of the flowers. The receptacle is highly-developed in the Compositae.

Resupinate. Appearing by a 180° twist of the axis to be upside-down or reversed (as the flowers of many orchids).

Revolute. Rolled downward, as the margin of a laminar organ.

Rhizome. A modified stem that grows horizontally underground; often serves as a deposit for reserve food material.

Root. A portion of the plant body of a seed plant, lacking nodes, buds and leaves; usually underground, it is used by the

plant as an organ of anchorage and for absorbing water and nutritive substances.

Rosette. A cluster of leaves, often overlapping, growing out in all directions around a single center point. May be either basal or apical.

Ruderal. Or a species of vegetation growing in an environment greatly modified by man.

Samara. A dry indehiscent fruit with a broad wing that facilitates scattering of the seeds by the wind.

Scape. Often leafless, flower-bearing axis.

Scarious. Thin and membranous in texture, as of a bract.

Sclerenchyma. A protective supportive tissue in higher plants composed of cells with walls that are thickened and lignified and often mineralized.

Sclerophyll. A plant with broad, leathery, persistent leaves with much sclerenchymatous tissue, resulting in rather rigid foliage.

Scrub. Of a stunted tree or shrub growing to maximum 5 meters with a single, but non-dominant, stem, giving the appearance of equal height and breadth; a vegetation formation dominated by such individuals.

Semi-parasite. A parasitic plant containing some chlorophyll and therefore capable of some photosynthesis, but nevertheless forced to parasitize another plant to procure necessary nutrients.

Semi-amplexicaul. Of a petiole or leaf base that partially surrounds the axis on which it is borne.

Sepal. A single element of the calyx of a flower.

Sessile. Unstalked; an organ (flower, leaf, fruit, etc.) joined directly to its support, with no peduncle.

Sheath. The lower part of the leaf surrounding the stem.

Shrub. A several-stemmed woody plant, in which no one axis dominates over the others.

Siliqua. A dry dehiscent fruit longer than it is broad, composed of two carpels, that at maturity opens along two longitudinal lines; typical of the family Cruciferae.

Spadix. An inflorescence formed of an elongated fleshy axis bearing unisexual flowers. Typical of the Araceae.

Spathe. A bract of variable color and size, subtending an inflorescence.

Spatulate. Spatula-shaped, narrow at the base and widest toward the apex.

Species. Basic unit of zoological and botanical classification ranking immediately below a genus or subgenus, comprised of interbreeding organisms that ordinarily comprise differentiated populations.

Speculum. A glabrous patch of various form and color, differing from the remainder of the

labellum, typical of many orchids.
Spike. An inflorescence formed of an axis bearing, laterally, sessile or sub-sessile flowers.
Spine. A stiff, sharply-pointed organ derived from modification of a leaf, stipule, root, stem or branch.
Spore. A generally unicellular structure the function of which is to reproduce and spread the species; typical of the fungi and the ferns.
Spur. A tubular extension of the corolla or the calyx of a flower.
Stalk. Axis, stem.
Stamen. One of the male elements of the reproductive apparatus of a flower, consisting of a stalk or filament supporting the anther.
Station. An area of variable size that is uniform from the point of view of the ecological parameters referred to the physical environment.
Stem. A generally aerial plant part that supports secondary branches, leaves, etc.
Stigma. The tip of the style to which pollen grains adhere.
Stipule. A leaf- or scale-like structure of varying form and size located at the base of the leaf.
Stria. A minute groove or channel or a stripe or line distinguished by color, texture, etc.
Strobilus. A structure typical of the conifers (pines, firs, etc.) composed of scales or bracts bearing the male or female reproductive organs, arranged on a central axis.
Style. The stalk that connects the stigma to the ovary.
Suborbiculate. Approximately circular.
Subsessile. Nearly sessile, with a suggestion of a peduncle.
Subshrub. A plant similar to a shrub but with stems that are lignified only at the base and with herbaceous annual shoots.
Subspecies. Unit of classification ranking immediately below a species, designated on the basis of constant discriminating characters but also separated geographically or ecologically.
Succulent. Having fleshy tissues containing water.
Sucker. A vigorous shoot originating from the roots or lower part of the stem of a plant.
Suffruticose. See **subshrub**.
Symbiosis. The living together of two dissimilar organisms in mutually beneficial relationships.

Tepal. Any of the modified leaves making up the perianth of a flower when petals (generally colored) and sepals (generally green) are not distinguishable in the corolla.
Thermomediterranean: Hot Mediterranean climate; the term also refers to the plants that live in areas characterized by this type of climate.
Tomentose. Covered with cottony downy hairs.

Tomentum. Pubescence composed of matted wooly hairs.
Toothed. Serrated; refers to leaf or petal margins.
Transpiration. The emission of water vapor from the surface tissues of living organisms; especially, from the surfaces of leaves and other parts of plants.
Tree. A woody perennial plant, generally large in size, having one erect main axis or stem dominating the others; generally taller than it is wide.
Tube. An often cylindrical, fused part of a corolla or calyx; typical of the Compositae.
Tuber. A swollen underground stem serving as a reserve for nutrients.
Two-lipped. Of the calyx or corolla of a flower divided into two parts, one upper and one lower. The two-lipped corolla is typical of the Labiatae (oregano, thyme, sage).
Two-pinnate. Of a leaf divided into segments which in turn are divided into segments.

Umbel. An inflorescence in which the flowers are all at the same level and the flower stalks all arise from the same point, like the spokes of an umbrella.
Unilateral. Of an inflorescence in which the single flowers are arranged all on one side.
Unisexual. Of a flower with only stamens or only a pistil.

Vegetation. Group of individuals belonging to one or more species that share the water, light and nutritive resources of a given space at a given time.
Verticil. A circle or whorl of similar parts (as flowers or leaves) about a point on an axis.
Verticillaster. A mixed inflorescence composed of a pair of opposite cymes arising at more or less the same point on the axis, resembling a true verticil. Typical of many members of the family Labiatae.
Villous. Densely covered with fine, long hairs.
Vulnerary. Promoting the healing of wounds and sores.

Weed. An introduced, fast-growing herbaceous plant that infests cultivated land and subtracts nutritive substances, water and light to the detriment of the crop.
Whorl. More than two organs arising at the same point on the stem, as flowers or leaves.

Xeric. Very dry; generally referred to a climate or a substrate.
Xerophytic. An ecological type referred to plants adapted for life and growth in xeric climates.

COMMON ENGLISH NAMES USED IN TEXT

Anemone, Crown: *Anemone coronaria.*
Asphodel: *Asphodelus* spp.
Asphodel, Common: *Asphodelus aestivus.*
Asphodel, Yellow: *Asphodeline lutea.*

Bay, Sweet: *Laurus nobilis.*
Bellflower: *Campanula* spp.
Bindweed, Mallow-Leaved: *Convolvulus althaeoides.*
Broom: *Cytisus* spp.
Buttercup: *Ranunculus* spp.

Candytuft, Burnt: *Aethionema saxatile.*
Carob: *Ceratonia siliqua.*
Chaste Tree: *Vitex agnus-castus.*
Cistus: *Cistus* spp.
Cistus, Sage-Leaved: *Cistus salviifolius*
Cucumber, Squirting: *Ecballium elaterium.*
Cypress, Italian: *Cupressus sempervirens* var. *horizontalis.*

Daffodil, Sea: *Pancratium maritimum.*
Daisy, Crown: *Chrysanthemum coronarium.*

Fennel, Giant: *Ferula communis* L. subsp. *communis.*

Gladiolus, Field: *Gladiolus italicus.*
Goat's-Beard: *Tragopogon sinuatus.*
Grape Hyacinth: *Muscari spreitzenhoferi.*

Heath, Sea: *Frankenia* spp.
Holly, Sea: *Eryngium maritimum.*
Horned-Poppy, Yellow: *Glaucium flavum.*
Hound's Tongue, Blue: *Cynoglossum creticum.*

Iris, Algerian: *Iris unguicularis* Poir. subsp. *cretensis.*

Juniper, Prickly: *Juniperus oxycedrus* subsp. *macrocarpa.*
Juniper, Phoenician: *Juniperus phoenicea*

Laurel: *Laurus nobilis.*
Lentisc: *Pistacia lentiscus.*
Lily, Sea: *Pancratium maritimum.*
Love-in-a-Mist: *Nigella damascena.*
Lupin: *Lupinus* spp.
Lupin, White: *Lupinus albus.*

Marjoram, Pot: *Origanum onites.*
Mastic Tree: *Pistacia lentiscus.*
Milkwort: *Polygala* spp.
Monk's Pepper: *Vitex agnus-castus.*
Myrtle, Common: *Myrtus communis* subsp. *communis.*
Oak, Kermes: *Quercus coccifera.*
Oleander: *Nerium oleander.*
Olive: *Olea europaea.*
Orchid, Man: *Aceras anthropophorum.*

Orchid: *Anacamptis, Aceras, Ophrys, Orchis, Serapias.*

Palm, Cretan: *Phoenix theophrasti.*
Pear, Almond-Leaved: *Pyrus spinosa.*
Phlomis: *Phlomis* spp.
Phlomis: *Phlomis* spp.
Plane: *Platanus orientalis.*
Plantain: *Plantago* spp.

Sage, Jerusalem: *Phlomis fruticosa.*
Sandalwood: *Osyris alba.*
Selaginella, Mediterranean: *Selaginella denticulata.*
Skullcap: *Scutellaria* spp.
Sowbread, Cretan: *Cyclamen creticum.*
Spurge: *Euphorbia* spp.
Spurge, Tree: *Euphorbia dendroides.*
Spurge, Sea: *Euphorbia paralias.*
Spurge, Large Mediterranean: *Euphorbia characias.*
Spurge, Greek Spiny: *Euphorbia acanthothamnos.*

Thistle, Globe: *Echinops* spp.
Thistle, Milk: *Silybum marianum.*

Venus's Looking Glass, Large: *Legousia speculum-veneris.*
Viper's-Grass, Cretan: *Scorzonera cretica.*

Water Dropwort, Corky-Fruited: *Oenanthe pimpinelloides.*

ABBREVIATIONS

spp.: various species (ex.: *Limonium* spp. = various species of *Limonium*).
subsp.: subspecies.
var.: variety.

INDEX

BIBLIOGRAPHY

Baumann H., *Greek Wild Flowers and Plant Lore in Ancient Greece*, The Herbert Press, London 1993.

Bayer E., Buttler K.P., Finkenzeller X., Grau J., *Guide de la flore méditerranéenne*, Delachaux et Niestlé, Lousanne 1990.

Di Castri F., Goodall D. W. & Specht R. L., *Mediterranean-type shrublands*, Elsevier Scientific Company, Amsterdam 1981.

Greuter W., Burdet H. M. Long G., *Med-cheklist*, vol. 1, 3, 4, Genève 1984-89.

Iatridis Y., *Flowers of Crete*, Iatridis Y, Athens 1985.

Lippert W., Podlech D., *Piante mediterranee*, Ed. Giorgio Mondadori, Milano 1991.

Polunin O., *Flowers of Greece and the Balkans. A field guide*, Oxford University Press, Oxford 1980.

Schonfelder I., Schonfelder P., *La flora mediterranea*, Istituto Geografico De Agostini, Novara 1996.

Sfikas G., *Wild Flowers of Crete*, Efstathiadis Group, Athens 1987.

Turland N.J., Chilton L., Press J.R., *Flora of Cretan Area*, annoted Checklist and Atlas, HMSO, London 1993.

Tutin T.G. et alii, *Flora europaea*, voll.1-5, Cambridge University Press, Cambridge 1964-1980.

Zohary M., *Geobotanical foundations of the Middle East*, Springer Verlag, Stuttgart 1973.